KU-330-277

PELICAN BOOKS

A854

UNDERSTANDING THE EARTH

Dr Ronald Fraser has been closely connected with the science of geophysics for the past thirty years. As a member of the Research Department of the Alkali Division of I.C.I. he used geophysical methods to explore the salt beds of Cheshire; as scientific adviser in the British Element of the Control Commission for Germany he helped to organize a survey of the earth's crust and upper mantle in western Europe, taking advantage of the artificial earthquakes triggered by the explosion of war-time ammunition dumps; and as Administrative Secretary of the International Council of Scientific Unions he was involved in the forward planning of the International Geophysical Year (1957–8) and subsequently of the recent International Indian Ocean Expedition (1960–65). His other books include *Once Round The Sun* (1957) and *Planet Earth* (1961).

Dr Fraser now lives in New Zealand.

RONALD FRASER

UNDERSTANDING
THE EARTH

PENGUIN BOOKS

Penguin Books Ltd, Harmondsworth, Middlesex, England
Penguin Books Inc., 3300 Clipper Mill Road, Baltimore, Md 21211, U.S.A.
Penguin Books Australia Ltd, Ringwood, Victoria, Australia

—

First published as *The Habitable Earth* by Hodder & Stoughton 1964
This revised edition published in Pelican Books 1967
Copyright © Ronald Fraser, 1964

—

Made and printed in Great Britain
by Hazell Watson & Viney Ltd
Aylesbury, Bucks
Set in Monotype Plantin

For
ALLAN AND BILL
with love and gratitude

Contents

List of Plates

Acknowledgements

THE considerable revision of the original 1964 text which was needed to bring it reasonably up to date was carried out in Wellington, New Zealand; and here I am glad to acknowledge the advice, and timely help in the provision of library facilities, of the Geophysics Division and Oceanographic Institute of the N.Z. Department of Scientific and Industrial Research.

Acknowledgement is due for permission to include reproductions of the following new figures in the present text: to Interscience Publishers, for Fig. 49; to the Royal Society of London for Figs. 9, 41a, 44, 47, 54; to *Science*, for Figs. 51 and 52, both copyright 1964 by the American Association for the Advancement of Science; to *Science Journal*, for Fig. 58.

Figs. 5, 15, 38, 42, 44, 45, 49, 53, 54 and 74 have been drawn specially for this edition; otherwise line drawings are the work of the late Jack Worsley.

Among the written sources I have gone to for information, I should like to acknowledge my particular debt to the following: Beno Gutenberg, *Physics of the Earth's Interior* (Academic Press, 1959); Jacobs, Russell and Tuzo Wilson, *Physics and Geology* (McGraw Hill, 1959); John H. Hodgson, *Earthquakes and Earth Structure* (Prentice Hall Inc., 1964); Francis P. Shepard, *The Earth Beneath the Sea* (Oxford University Press, 1959); W. S. von Arx, *Introduction to Physical Oceanography* (Addison-Wesley Publishing Company, 1962); and A. E. M. Nairn, *Descriptive Paleoclimatology* (Interscience Publishers Ltd., 1961); also to the invaluable résumés of *Scientific American*.

Introduction

UNTIL the earthquake-hunters took over, man's knowledge of the structure of his pear-shaped planet was confined to the more superficial regions of the earth's crust. The tools of the classical geology of the nineteenth century – the heyday of the great pioneers like Chambers and Lyell and Geikie – were the geologist's hammer and the bit-borer of the oil-well.

It is therefore hardly surprising that such a limited range of observational techniques, applied moreover exclusively to the outermost skin of the granitic rafts which are the earth's land masses, should have led to quite a few wrong conclusions about the earth as a whole.

Thus today the following nineteenth-century notions have been publicly discarded by all forward-looking geologists: a cooling and shrinking globe; crustal shortening; conventional theories of mountain building; the ocean basins as submerged land masses, where one might seek the lost Atlantis.

The history of the scientific exploration of the interior of the earth is synonymous with the history of the development of the science of *seismology*, the study of earthquakes by the earthquake-hunters, the *seismologists*, who detect and record the earth tremors arising from sporadic dislocations in the solid substance of the earth.

The seismologists have set up a world network of *seismographs* – instruments cunningly designed to respond to the passage beneath them of the *seismic waves* which radiate from the focus of each and every earthquake – and they read into the messages received on their *seismograms* a specification of the internal structure of the globe.

The story of this major cooperative undertaking begins in 1897 with Richard Oldham of the Geological Society of London, who was the first to distinguish *two kinds* of seismic wave, the so-called P and S waves described in Chapter 1. Then came the patient analysis of the enormous mass of data accumulated by the seismographs of a score of different countries, culminating in 1940 with the publication of the *J–B Tables* by Sir Harold Jeffreys of Cambridge, England, and his pupil Keith Bullen of Sydney, Australia, of the travel times from source to seismograph of thousands of earthquakes, deep and shallow, large and small. These celebrated tables, when deciphered with the X-ray eyes of the seismologist, describe in astonishingly fine detail the internal structure of the earth.

Thus the *J–B Tables* of 1940 demonstrated beyond cavil the existence of a *liquid inner core*, surrounded by a massive *semi-plastic 'mantle'*, the whole sheathed by the thin *crust* of the continents and ocean floor. Crust, mantle, and inner liquid core: and to these must be added a small *central core*, first spotted by Miss I. Lehmann of Copenhagen in Denmark as early as 1936, in her classical analysis of the P and S waves radiating from two several earthquakes in New Zealand; and ten years later shown by Bullen to be *solid*.

Next, Beno Gutenberg of Pasadena in California, as the result of a detailed examination of a series of comparatively shallow quakes, demonstrated in 1953 the existence of the so-called 'Gutenberg channel' – a narrow zone in the upper mantle in which the substance of the mantle is less rigid and more plastic than is that of the remainder.

In 1952 there occurred a world-shaking earthquake in the mantle beneath Kamchatka in Eastern Siberia, which gave Hugo Benioff, a pupil of Gutenberg, furiously to think – of the earth ringing as one large spherical bell; and which led C. L. Pekeris in Israel to calculate the natural modes of vibration of an earth constructed on the model proposed by Bullen–Gutenberg – solid central core, liquid inner core, solid-mantle-sandwich with a plastic filling near the top, thin crust of basaltic rock under the oceans, granites and schists and gneisses and their detritus below the superficial surface of the land masses.

The prospect of such a verification of his ideas excited Bullen, in the course of his Einstein Memorial Lecture at Adelaide on 1 October 1959, to exclaim, with rare scientific detachment: 'We should like a few more world-shaking earthquakes to be sure that Benioff's observations are indeed genuine'! Well, his wish was granted in the Chile earthquake of 22 May 1960, which as we shall see verified the correctness of the 'B–G model' in every detail.

And finally, in the atomic age, with Bullen as foreman, the seismologists are busy beating yet another lethal sword into a pacific ploughshare. Atomic explosions, particularly those below ground, are the ideal seismological tool; because the *time of initiation* of the resulting artificial quake is known to a split second, instead of having to be inferred, as is the case with the vast majority of natural earthquakes.

Thus today the instant of detonation of a test bomb buried below ground in say the Nevada desert is made public property, in marked contrast to the childish secrecy which for years surrounded the times of explosion of the Bikini bombs in March, April and May 1954 – which anyway were deduced in short order by Bullen with an accuracy of the order of a fifth of a second. So we may perhaps be allowed the hope that the atom bomb will join bows and arrows, pikes, halberds, boiling lead, chain shot, hand grenades and tank traps on the scrap heap of our war museums; but that controlled underground atomic explosions, harmless to man or beast, may lead to a still more detailed knowledge than we have today of the internal structure of our home-in-space – Mother Earth.

For, as we shall learn in this book, mankind is indeed her child, sheltered and sustained by her mantle.

Thus in Chapter 1 is set out in detail much of what the seismologists have taught us about the interior of the globe; something of the elegant demonstration by Bullard of Cambridge that the magnetic field of the earth can be matched with that of a self-sustaining dynamo lodged in the liquid inner core; and of how earth's crust can now be differentiated, as between a thin ocean floor of primitive heavy basaltic rock, and continents composed mainly of considerably less dense granites, with of course secondary, sedimentary geological formations.

In Chapter 2 we shall learn about the long history of the formation of the continents in four great stages of mountain building, the material for which all came from the mantle: we shall see how the age of the rocks can be dated in time by nature's own radio-active clocks; and we shall trace on the globe a gigantic letter T, which marks out a world-wide zone of compressional fracture of the crust.

Chapter 3 deals with the rugged topography of the ocean floor: and here we shall discover, with Bruce Heezen of the Lamont Geological Observatory outside New York, a world-encompassing zone of tensional splitting; for he has found a great rift valley atop that gigantic range of under-water mountains which have their roots in the ocean bottom, and which snake their way in mid-ocean between the continents.

In Chapter 4 is presented evidence that the poles could well have wandered in their time over a goodly area of the earth's surface; that today the tracks traced out by the ancient poles over the map of the several continents don't match any more; and how this points to a drift of the continental icebergs as they float in the plastic 'ocean' of the upper mantle. It is shown further that this pointer to continental drift is matched by another – the direction in space relative to the earth's axis of the 'fossil magnets' which are found embedded in the two-hundred-million-year-old rocks of the Mesozoic era: that a consistent account of continental drift can be given on the assumption that the continents have been guided to their present stations on the map by slow-moving convection currents in the mantle; and how we may be approaching the final phase of this age-long process, when the continents shall at last drop anchor for the rest of their terrestrial life.

Finally, Chapter 5 reviews our present knowledge of earth's thin outer sheath of ocean water and 'this most excellent canopy the air'; how both 'the sky above (and) the sea with its bounds' are, equally with the continental mountains and the volcanic cones of the Pacific, products of the mantle; and how the sun powers the mighty heat engine of ocean: atmosphere, governing alike the winds aloft and the deep ocean currents.

In summarizing thus the achievements of the twentieth-century geophysicist, we see very clearly that he is no long-haired scientist in an ivory tower: he is an adventurer in the modern scientific exploration of our planet – no longer an affair of the opening-up of dark continents or the scaling of inaccessible mountain peaks, but of charting, with the aid of the most highly developed instruments of a sophisticated technology, both the deep interior of the earth and the unseen relief of the ocean floor; as also the atmosphere and the oceans.

So let us all – man and woman, boy and girl – rejoice with him, and with the Spirit of Wisdom, in the habitable part of the earth – climbing its mountain peaks, 'running schuss' on skis down the snow-clad slopes of its valleys, exploring the green hills of Africa after lion and antelope, sailing a dinghy before a wind that follows fast; or banking a Moth at three thousand feet under a blue sky and looking down from an open cockpit on a chequer-board of field and moorland and parkland and lake and then shutting off and gliding in the whisper of one's own slip-stream down back over the trees and the housetops to a happy landing in the waiting meadow.

CHAPTER ONE

Crust, Mantle and Core

FIVE thousand million years ago the sun and its planets, of which the earth is one, were born as a spinning cloud of interstellar gas and stardust, out on a limb of our galaxy, the Milky Way.

Such is the testimony of the stars, as deciphered from their present colour and brightness by the astronomers. The infant sun was however very different from the blazing nuclear power station we recognize it to be today: even 4,000 million years ago it was still only a ball of hydrogen and some heavier elements, its diameter that of the present orbit of Mercury, its temperature colder than ice. The surrounding planetary nebula was even colder; to be precise, more than 200°C below the freezing point of water.

PROTO-EARTH

Now any such spinning cloud of cold gas-dust mixture is obliged to shrink to the form of a rotating disc. The shrinkage of the planetary nebula brought with it therefore an increase in material density which could locally override the gravitational authority of the already contracting central sun. The disc began to break up by local gravitational accretion into separate rotating clouds, the proto-planets, of which proto-earth was one – a clot of star-dust a little warmer than the pristine nebula, but still only some 40°C above absolute zero.

Another 500 million years, and the sun began to shrink under the pull of its own gravity. And no sooner did its hydrogen atoms get together than up went its temperature. The shrinking sun, fed by the same potent nuclear processes which are all too familiar to mankind today in the hydrogen bomb, started to transmit sunlight on its present visible and ultra-violet wavelengths. Consequently, the tenuous gas between the proto-planets was swept clean away by the new broom of the radiant sun, by the pressure of sunlight, just as today we can observe how the comets' tails are pushed outwards as they approach the sun.

Once interplanetary space had been swept clear by the nascent sun, the now spherical proto-planets – including of course the earth – came under a fierce bombardment of atomic

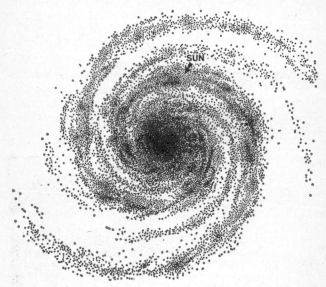

Fig. 1. Our place in the sun, out on an arm of our spiral galaxy – the Milky Way.

particles – protons and electrons – and of the immaterial photons of visible and ultra-violet light, emitted by the sun; with the inevitable result that they forthwith proceeded to lose a greater or lesser proportion of their more volatile components by evaporation into the surrounding space.

And proto-earth, the greater part of its primeval gases blasted off into outer space, shrank to form a compact central ball of much the same chemical composition as the earth we live on today. The result was that its core melted, under the combined effects of the release of gravitational energy which must follow any such contraction and of the heat generated by the entrapped radio-active elements.

Then, over a period of perhaps another 1,000 million years, came the gradual cooling of the white-hot interior by radiation through its thick skin into outer space, and a radial separation into a highly compressed central solid core, a liquid inner core, a semi-plastic mantle, and a primeval basaltic crust, the present phase of which is illustrated in Fig. 2.

Here the words 'present phase' are used advisedly, for the separation of the liquid nickel-iron core from the surrounding mantle has probably been a gradual process, which may indeed only now be entering on its final stage. Thus 3,000 million years ago the radius of the liquid core may well have been only a tenth of its present value: a supposition which will reveal itself as of fundamental importance in the sequel.

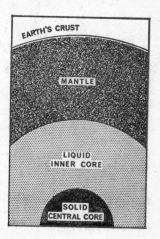

Fig. 2. The interior of the earth as revealed by the earthquake-hunters: a central solid core, composition unknown, radius 800 miles; an inner core of nickel-iron, estimated density 10·5, held molten at a temperature of 1,000°C under pressures of the order of a million atmospheres, outer radius 2,150 miles; a rocky mantle, composed of silicates of magnesium, estimated average density 4·3, thickness 1,800 miles; and the thin crust we can explore from the surface.

EARTHQUAKES GALORE

The detailed knowledge of the interior structure of the earth, epitomized in Fig. 2, has been won, in the main over the past sixty years or so, from a systematic study of earthquakes. The prototype of the modern earthquake-hunter (or seismologist) is the Indian brave, listening with his ear to the ground for the approaching footfall of the enemy. In every scientifically developed country of the world there are 'listening posts': seismological stations, equipped with sensitive seismographs which register the arrival – as earth tremors – of the seismic waves radiated in all directions from the point of origin, or focus, of each and every earthquake.

One of the more widely used *seismometers* – by which is meant the instrument that *detects* earthquakes, as distinct from the recording apparatus – is illustrated in Plate 4, which shows the Willmore seismometer Mark I, produced by Hilger and Watts (London) around 1950. The Mark II, dating from 1963, is a considerable improvement on its predecessor; and the technical particulars given in the caption to Plate 4 refer to it. The important principle in the design of the 'Willmore', however, is that the coil is fixed to the frame of the instrument, while the spring-mounted magnet rises and falls with the crests and troughs of a seismic wave passing through the earth below it.

We have referred to the Willmore as one of the *more* widely used seismometers. It would seem, however, that before very long the *most* widely used instruments will be a short-period seismometer (1 second) designed by Hugo Benioff; and one of longer period (15 seconds), known as the 'Press-Ewing' seismometer, like that used with such spectacular success at Palisades (New York) in the detection of the Chile earthquake of 1960 (see Fig. 12).

For these are the instruments which at the close of the year 1965 were installed at upwards of 150 seismic stations, cunningly located on the map of the world, as part of an international system of standardized equipment and procedure conjured into being by Lloyd Berkner, the man who first suggested an International Geophysical Year. This network, familiarly known as 'WWSS' (World-Wide Standard System), replaces the haphazard collection of instrumental types which made the correct interpretation and comparison of seismograms such a tricky job in the past.

SEISMIC WAVES

Seismic waves come in two varieties, known in the jargon of seismology as P waves and S waves respectively.

P (for 'principle') waves are like sound waves in air: they are waves of alternating *compression* and dilatation – 'concertina waves', if you will.

S (for 'secondary') waves are like (and yet unlike) water waves, in so far as they are transverse waves with their crests and troughs rising and falling at right angles to the direction of propagation. They can be propagated only in media possessing a finite *rigidity*; liquids are therefore excluded as transmitters of S waves.

P waves travel faster than S waves; their average velocity is around 8 km/sec, as against around 4.5 km/sec for S waves.

The *time of passage* of seismic waves, from focus through mantle and liquid inner core to observation station, is of the order of seconds. Thus the properties of *compressibility* and *rigidity* assigned to the mantle, and of compressibility to the liquid core, are those of matter effectively under *instantaneous stress*. It cannot be emphasized too strongly that the numerical values assigned to the two parameters of compressibility and rigidity are valid only for a *rapid* build-up of stress, and its equally rapid release, such as are met with in seismology. They do *not* necessarily refer to the properties of the mantle when subject to stress over the geological time-scale of millions of years rather than seconds of time. Indeed, there is ample evidence that within such a geological time-scale, the mantle ceases to be an *elastic* solid, and becomes subject to the well-known creep-under-small-stresses which characterizes *plastic* solids.

For the moment, however, since we are discussing transient seismological phenomena, the mantle may be assumed to be an elastic solid, characterized mathematically by two coefficients – that of *incompressibility* (i.e. the reciprocal of compressibility), and of *rigidity*, which determine the velocity of the shock waves radiating in all directions from the focus of an earthquake.

In common with any other kind of wave motion, seismic waves

are refracted, or bent, at the boundary between two different media. But whereas light waves, with which we are most familiar, travel more slowly in a dense medium, such as glass, than in a less dense medium like air, the reverse is the case for seismic waves. The result is that whereas light is deflected towards the base of a glass prism, a P wave would be deflected towards its apex.

Now suppose a major earthquake occurs at a point in the mantle lying beneath the North Pole. Seismographs stationed anywhere north of latitude 15°S would record the arrival first of P waves, then of S waves; the more sensitive seismographs situated between 15°S and 52°S would record very feeble P waves, but no S waves; while at those which lie south of 52°S the P waves would come in 'loud and clear' once more.

And now for the interpretation of the so-called 'shadow zone', which is a feature common to all earthquakes, no matter where their centres of activity may be located.

In the first place, the fade-out of the P waves inside the shadow zone means that they must have encountered a large

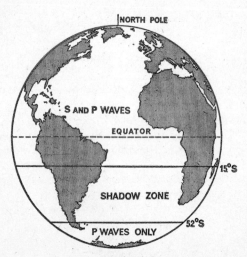

Fig. 3. The pattern of P and S seismic waves received at the earth's surface from an earthquake having its focus in the mantle immediately below the north pole.

central core in the interior of the earth in which their velocity is sharply reduced, causing them to be bent abruptly *inwards* at the boundary between the mantle in which they originated and the core. In the second place the total disappearance of the S waves at the margin of the shadow zone can only mean that the inner core is *liquid;* for, as we have seen, a liquid is ruled out as a medium for the propagation of S waves. And finally, the appearance of weak P waves *inside* the shadow zone reveals

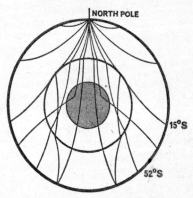

Fig. 4. The shadow zone of Fig. 3, properly interpreted, leads immediately to the picture of the earth's interior illustrated in Fig. 2.

the presence of a *small solid core*, which bends the P waves *outwards* at its boundary.

This clear picture of the interior of the earth, even if it is admitted that the separate pieces of the jigsaw have been picked up by many workers in the field over a period of many years, is due primarily to the uncanny insight of one man – Keith Bullen. Indeed, it is known in the trade as 'the Bullen B model': we shall meet it again in the sequel.

WHY EARTHQUAKES?

That is the 'how' of earthquakes, easily written down in a sentence. The fundamental question of 'why' calls for rather more extended discussion.

Earthquakes are classified according to the depth below surface at which the causative disturbance in the material of either crust or mantle occurs. The point (or more properly, the restricted region) where 'first motion' occurs is called the *focus*, and the point on the earth's surface perpendicularly above the focus is called the *epicentre* of the consequent earthquake.

Earthquakes are classed as *shallow* when their foci are located at depths up to say 50 km; *intermediate* for foci which are anywhere between 50 and 300 km below surface; and *deep* if the focal depth is over 300 km.

Thus those earthquakes classified as either 'intermediate' or 'deep' have their foci located *within the substance of the mantle:*

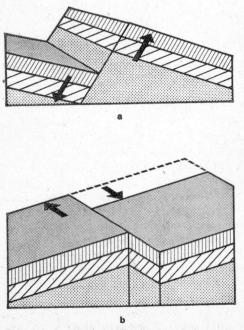

Fig. 5. Faults: (*a*) the standard 'vertical fault' of classical geology; and (*b*) an impression of a 'transcurrent fault', of which the most striking example is the San Andreas fault in California (see Plate 19).

only for the shallowest of earthquakes is the focus located in the crustal rocks. Yet the notion persists in modern seismological thinking, particularly in the West, that *all* earthquakes are triggered by the sudden release of something akin to 'elastic strain' – a term quite properly used by geologists when it is stored at the interface between two adjacent blocks of solid rock. The notion then is one of *faulting*: and the result is a plethora of 'models' of first motion, such as the uni-planar model, the quadrantal model, and so forth.

Now for shallow earthquakes we might agree to accept the fault theory as reasonable; although even here we might argue with Frank Evison of Wellington, New Zealand, that it could equally well be the earthquake which triggered the fault. But for deep-focus earthquakes the idea of 'faulting' within the heterogeneous substance of the mantle is a little difficult to visualize.

It is not enough, however, merely to entertain a doubt (some might say prejudice) about faulting as the primary cause of earthquakes – we must seek, and find if we can, the true nature of the first movement which triggers them.

Now the shallowest of earthquakes, having foci at depths less than say 8 km, have been intensively (and expensively) studied in both Britain and the United States ever since the 1958 Disarmament Conference at Geneva, in a partially successful attempt to distinguish them from man-made nuclear explosions. The object of the exercise has been of course to advance the cause of a comprehensive Test Ban Treaty. Whether or not this aim be achieved, the correlative advances in seismological technique as such have been tremendous. Yet even here, opinion remains divided as to whether the difference between a natural earthquake and the explosion of a buried A-bomb, which show up on the elaborately processed seismograms, are due to differences in the source mechanism or to difference in the geological surroundings of the source.

Be that as it may, Evison and others have been led to postulate that first movement for all but the shallowest earthquakes is akin to an explosion (or alternatively implosion) in the substance of the mantle: specifically as one set off by a sudden phase change in the crystal structure of the silicates – say from spinel to olivine, or vice versa – of a restricted volume of the earth's interior.

Properly to understand the meaning of this new idea, we must first examine rather more closely what is known or surmised about the detailed crystalline structure of the mantle. Here, then, in the geochemist's shorthand, is a summary of informed contemporary opinion in this regard:

From the base of the Crust to a depth of 100 km: A crystal mix of Mg_2SiO_4 (olivine) and $MgSiO_3$ (pyroxene).

From a depth of 100 km to a depth of 1,000 km: A graded change with depth from the comparatively open crystal structure of pyroxene and olivine to the more closely packed structure of spinel and ilmenite:

100 km

$2MgSiO_3$ (pyroxene) $\rightarrow Mg_2SiO_4$ (olivine) $+ SiO_2$ (steshovite)

Mg_2SiO_4 (olivine) $\rightarrow Mg_2SiO_4$ (spinel)

Mg_2SiO_4 (spinel) $\rightarrow SiO_2$ (steshovite) $+ 2MgSiO_3$ (ilmenite)

Mg_2SiO_4 (spinel) $\rightarrow MgSiO_3$ (ilmenite) $+ MgO$ (pericline)

1,000 km

From a depth of 1,000 km to a depth of 2,900 km: Maximum close-packing, no further phase change with increasing depth.

There are two significant points to observe in connexion with this dry-looking table: first, that no earthquake has so far been observed with a focal depth greater than 700 km, a figure which is near enough to the theoretical depth limit to phase change of 1,000 km: second, that the cumulative density-increases involved in the polymorphic transitions listed above – at least 20 per cent – is equivalent to an energy increase from a volume of about a cubic kilometre at a depth of 500 km, of not less than 5×10^{24} ergs; while the energy required to trigger a fair-sized earthquake is of the same order, namely not less than 10^{24} ergs.

Now Evison, in a recent analysis of well-attested earthquakes whose epicentres lie on the Pacific 'ring of fire', has come up with the following findings: the first motion for earthquakes whose epicentres lie below the deep ocean trenches is predominantly one of *dilatation;* for earthquakes whose epicentres lie at depths of less than 200 km. below the corresponding island arcs, the first motion is one of *compression*. Thus phase changes in the mantle leading to *implosions* are indicated for the trenches; while the rule is for *explosions* in the upper mantle beneath the uplifted islands of the corresponding arcs.

All this is in close agreement with the picture of the formation of the island arcs and trenches depicted in Chapter 2 below; and we shall find ourselves moreover with a livelier appreciation of the chiaroscuro which brushes in the downward movement of the plastic mantle beneath the trenches, leading to phase changes in the sense of a density increase; likewise the surfacing of the mantle in the volcanic uplift of the shoreward islands, leading to a decrease in the density of its polymorphic substance.

MICROSEISMS

Keith Bullen, in his beautifully written book *An Introduction to the Theory of Seismology*, has this to say about microseisms: 'In addition to ordinary earthquakes, seismograms at many observatories reveal the presence of additional small earth movements which are called *microseisms*. . . . The largest of the earth movements associated with these microseisms are of the order of one thousandth of a centimetre and occur in coastal regions. . . . There is a fair correlation between the size of the microseisms and the occurrence of stormy weather in some adjacent region. . . .'

The serious study of microseisms began among the meteorologists back in the forties: for they hoped thereby to learn how to track the approach of oceanic hurricanes to the densely inhabited areas on the eastern borders of the Atlantic and on the western coasts of the Pacific. The idea was that you could perform the seismic equivalent of sound ranging from two or more observing stations near the coast with the aid of the microseisms set up in the ocean floor beneath the 'eye' of an oceanic storm: for after all, argued the meteorologists, you couldn't expect to pull the stratosphere down to the surface of the sea and not expect a slight bump on the ocean bottom as a consequence.

Unfortunately, it turned out that the energy which the hurricanes can transmit to the ocean floor is normally only a small fraction of that concentrated in the eye of the storm; and anyway the all-seeing eye of Tiros and his modern successor Nimbus is an infinitely more efficient method of keeping track of a hurricane than any system of seismic listening posts (compare Plate 21).

However that may be, the seismologists continued to be intrigued by the search for a reasonable *theoretical mechanism*, which would explain in detail all the features of microseisms as observed at seismological stations situated on the continental coasts; and since 1950 their thinking has acknowledged the brilliant lead given by M.S. Longuet-Higgins, now of the British Oceanographic Institute.

Longuet-Higgins showed that microseisms were caused, not by 'pumping action' in the eye of an oceanic storm, as originally proposed, but the pressures transmitted under certain circumstances to the ocean floor by the surface *swell waves* sent out over the sea from the moving centre of the hurricane. True, such microseisms in the substance of the deep ocean floor may die out as they strike the continental slope; but those observed at the coastal stations can be generated *de novo* by the approaching swell waves *at the shoreward margin of the continental shelf*. He showed moreover that the seismograms recorded at the coastal stations were to be attributed, not primarily to the swell waves, but to the *standing waves* set up in the water above the continental shelf by the *reflection* of the swell waves at the coast-line, whether that were topographically beetling cliff or shelving beach. Most intriguing of all, his mathematics demanded that the period of these coastal microseisms should be half that of the swell waves which gave rise to them, which was precisely what previous observations had shown to be the case.

So much for the theoretical reasoning of Longuet-Higgins, incidentally the subject of at times heated debate among seismologists throughout the fifties. In the end, an elegant confirmation of the theory came from observations made from January to December 1958 in the Ross Sea by Trevor Hatherton, as part of New Zealand's contribution to the Antarctic programme of the International Geophysical Year.

Hatherton found that two distinct classes of microseisms were recorded by his seismographs at Scott Base on Ross Island. The first class showed up strongly only during the Antarctic summer – that is from January to June – when the Ross Sea was free of surface ice. The period of these locally generated microseisms was short, of the order of one to four seconds. They were clearly the offspring of choppy seas in the immediate neighbourhood of Ross Island: they ceased when the Ross Sea became ice-bound during the Antarctic winter.

The second class of microseisms observed by Hatherton were of longer period – 4 to 10 seconds. They attained their maximum amplitude during the months of March and April, when the entrance from the open ocean to the Ross Sea over the Antarctic continental shelf is effectively free of pack ice. Moreover, the individual long-period microseisms registered their arrival on Hatherton's seismograms in step with the appearance of centres of atmospheric depression over the open water north-west of the entrance to the Ross Sea, as reported to him by the U.S. Antarctic Weather Centre at Little America. The conclusion is well-nigh inescapable: namely that the long-period microseisms are generated on the continental shelf by swell waves created at the air-sea interface by the north-west winds of the Antarctic cyclones. This conclusion is supported by the values of the period of swell waves (8 to 14 seconds) as calculated from the measured cyclonic wind velocities of 16 to 27 metres/second: for these values are reasonably close to the theoretical value of twice the observed periods of the corresponding microseisms, namely 4 to 10 seconds.

BUILT-IN DYNAMO

Little more is known about the central solid core of the earth than its existence. It is quite otherwise, however, with the liquid inner core. Here the consensus of opinion is for a molten nickel-iron core under high pressure; for such a composition for the liquid inner core agrees well with the observed velocity of those earthquake P waves which traverse it, as also with the composition of meteorites – planetary fragments which have failed to coalesce by 'cold accretion' – which arrive on the earth's surface from interplanetary space. Moreover, it serves to explain the observed phenomena of the earth's magnetic field.

Now the observed terrestrial magnetic field can be broken down by mathematical analysis into a number of geocentric *magnetic dipoles*. A first approximation yields the familiar dipole inclined to the earth's axis of rotation at an angle of $11\frac{1}{2}°$ (see Fig. 6). This may be resolved into three dipoles at right angles, of which the *axial dipole* is by far the largest. Higher approximations give the *non-dipole* field – of which more in the sequel.

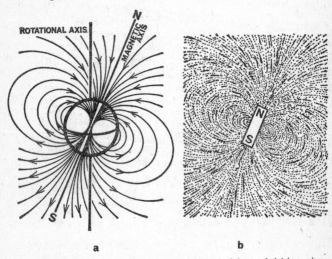

a   **b**

Fig. 6. To a first approximation, the magnetic field of the earth (*a*) is equivalent to that of a bar magnet (*b*).

Our immediate interest is the geocentric axial field; and here we ask ourselves the following question: Can we interpret the axial dipole field in terms of the properties of a molten nickel-iron core?

In recent years Bullard of Cambridge and Elsasser of La Jolla in California have suggested that the earth's axial field is that of a *self-exciting dynamo*, as illustrated in Fig. 7, whose seat lies in the motions of the substance of the liquid inner core. They argue that the heat transported outwards from the liquid inner core to the mantle and so outwards through the crust into space is to be accounted for, not only by conduction, but by *thermal convection* as well: that is, by the actual physical transport of the heated particles of the core radially from the outer boundary of the solid central core to the inner boundary of the mantle, and the return of the cooler particles from mantle to central core. In other words, they assume the existence of radially directed *convection cells* in the liquid inner core, and strive to match these with possible models of a self-exciting

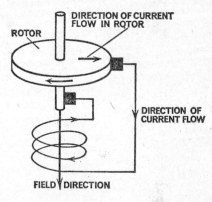

Fig. 7. A skeleton diagram of a self-exciting dynamo, such as in invoked in the liquid inner core to account for the earth's magnetic field.

dynamo which shall give rise to the observed external magnetic field of the earth.

A clear understanding of their argument demands an equally clear understanding of precisely how a self-exciting dynamo functions. So let us look more closely at Fig. 7.

Here, then, is a picture of a particular form of Faraday's 'disc dynamo', in which a circular sheet of copper spins above a coil of copper wire. If an electric current, however feeble, is once started in the coil, it acts like a bar magnet; and a *radially directed* sheet of electric current is immediately induced in the disc. If now we tap off this current by means of the upper brush you see in the figure, and lead it back into the bottom end of the coil via the lower brush, then clearly the cycle of events is in principle *self-sustaining*.

We write advisedly 'in principle', for there is a 'technical hitch' in the arrangement as it stands. The snag is this: that the copper disc is not a perfect conductor of electricity, so unless a small boosting current is injected into the circuit, the current in the disc will be sooner or later dissipated; in other words, converted into the thermal motion of its copper atoms.

There are two ways of getting round this difficulty: either by spinning the disc faster, or by increasing its radius; for it is the *radial velocity* – that is, the area of the circular disc swept out by a chosen radius in unit time – that counts.

Now the radius of the earth is amply long enough for this purpose, *if* there is indeed a self-exciting disc dynamo hidden in its liquid core: and it is this 'if' that Bullard and Gellman examined under the lens of mathematical analysis, in their classic contribution to the Philosophical Transactions of the Royal Society of London for the year 1954.

To this end, Bullard and Gellman begin by passing in review *all the possible motions* of the substance of the liquid inner core, *on the basic assumption of the existence of radially directed convection cells*.

On this premise, they argue that the convection cells are disposed radially only *ab initio*, for gyroscopic forces soon push them out of their *meridianal* planes into planes which are parallel with the *equatorial plane* of the earth: much as a gyro-compass is forced to rotate with its axis parallel to earth's axis of rotation.

There are numerous patterns in which the convection cells, thus stably oriented, could be arranged to give dynamo action. The simplest pattern is shown in Fig. 8(a), which illustrates the 'T2 pattern', or in the sophisticated language of the mathematical physicist 'the second toroidal mode'.

So far so good . . . But immediately the question arises: 'How can the random directions of the flow of liquid particles in the convection cells be transformed into the stream-lined circum-axial flow characteristic of the T2 pattern?' Answer: 'The pageant-master that lines up a jostling crowd of eddies into an ordered procession is the rotation of the earth': an answer that you must take on trust from the formidable mathematics which lies behind it.

Concentrate now on the T2 pattern, of stream-lined flow in planes parallel to the equatorial plane; and let us pose yet another question, namely 'What must be the electro-dynamical consequences of such an ordered motion of material particles in an electrically conducting medium such as is the nickel-iron inner core of the earth?'

To begin to answer this question, we must first make a digression into the science of magnetohydrodynamics, which deals with the interaction between a liquid or gaseous medium and an ambient magnetic field under just such conditions as are met with in the earth's liquid core: namely large volume and high pressure.

It turns out that in such a medium under such conditions, the lines of magnetic force are literally 'frozen into the material' – or 'bottled' if you like – and get carried along with it in any internal motion which may occur. This is what happens, therefore, to the lines of the earth's magnetic field when they get caught up in the streamlined flow of the T2 pattern: they are

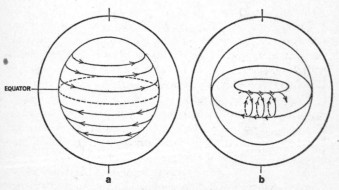

EQUATOR

a   b

Fig. 8. (a) The simplest pattern of stream-lines in the inner liquid core which could foster a self-exciting dynamo – the so-called 'T2 pattern'; (b) the resulting axial toroidal magnetic field, responsible for the external magnetic field of the earth. (After Bullard and Gellman.)

dragged along in the wake of the moving particles of the liquid core.

And here we recall that the dipole field of the earth, since it is not strictly lined up with the axis of rotation, possesses a *radial component*, just like the *ab initio* motion of the particles in the liquid core. Thus in passing from their initial motion in a radial direction to their martialled procession in the circum-axial stream-lined flow of the T2 pattern, the fluid particles exert a *lateral pull* on the frozen-in lines of magnetic force. Consequently, those sections of the radially directed component of the earth's field which are nearer to the centre of the earth get pulled aside less than do sections near the periphery of the core, where the tangential velocity of the moving particles is greater; and the lines of force get snarled up into corkscrew spirals around the stream-lines of the T2 pattern.

Projected on to the equatorial plane, therefore, is the resultant doughnut-shaped spiral, or *toroid*, to be seen in Fig. 8(b). Such a toroid of magnetic lines of force is strictly equivalent to a dipole field axial to the toroidal ring. Hence the earth's axial field, as a final consequence of the radial motion of the particles of the liquid core, as they transport heat by convection from the inner core outwards to the mantle.

To conclude the argument, back to our dynamo of Fig. 7. Fundamentally, what any dynamo does is to convert mechanical energy into electrical energy – whereas an electric *motor* does just the opposite, converting injected electrical energy into the mechanical energy of the rotor. And this is precisely what the application of the principles of magnetohydrodynamics teaches us about the goings-on in the earth's liquid core: for in coiling themselves around the stream-lines of the liquid flow, the lines of magnetic force *become stretched*. In so doing, *they gain mechanical energy:* for if they were freed from this constraint they would snap back straight again, just like a piece of elastic.

Our toroid, therefore, has gained electro-magnetic energy from the mechanical energy of the stretched lines of magnetic force; and this is the sign-manual of any dynamo.

Thus it can be fairly said that Bullard has demonstrated how the earth's magnetic field can indeed be attributed to a 'homogeneous dynamo' lodged in the earth's liquid inner core. This is not to say, however, that the dynamo mechanism is the only possible one; nor even then that the T2 pattern of fluid flow is the only pattern which could give rise to dynamo action. Nevertheless, comparison of the earth's magnetic field with say that of sunspots, where 'bottled magnetism' seems to offer the only possible explanation, leads us to rank the homogeneous dynamo mechanism very high as a working hypothesis in the understanding of the origins of the earth's magnetic field.

SURFACE EDDIES

Next, we examine the conditions which must exist at the boundary between the inner liquid core and its semi-solid sheath, where the T2 equatorial stream-lines brush the inner surface of the mantle.

As with any stream-lined flow of a liquid completely filling a solid container, we must expect to find *turbulent eddy-currents* in the outer layers of the liquid. And so indeed we do in the case of the liquid inner core: eddy-currents which reveal themselves at the earth's surface as local perturbations of the axial field of the steady toroidal currents in the core. A glance at Fig. 9, in which Bullard, following Vestine of Minneapolis in the United States, has charted the vertical component of the non-dipole field at different places on the globe, convinces one immediately of the truth of that statement.

Vestine for his part has plotted the values taken by the earth's *total* magnetic field (i.e., dipole field plus non-dipole field) at corresponding points on the earth's surface, from the year 1905 onwards: and he finds that the resulting contour patterns drift westward over the years at the rate of some 12 miles per annum.

Now this can only mean that crust and mantle are rotating from west to east at a greater speed than the core. And the reason is not far to seek: the inner mantle, composed as it is predominantly of iron-magnesium silicates, is a fair conductor of electricity. This means that core and mantle are electrically coupled, to the extent that the eddy-currents at the surface of the liquid

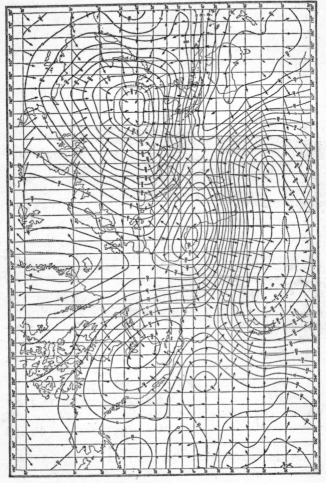

Fig. 9. The earth's non-dipole field in 1945. The contours give the vertical field, the arrows the horizontal component. (Bullard et al.)

core can leak into the substance of the lower mantle. The mantle thus becomes as it were the armature of an electric motor of which the field is the axial field of the earth, and so is driven eastward relative to the core; and we, as observers perched on the solid crust-mantle surface of the earth, interpret our eastward motion as a westward motion of the core and its eddy currents.

WRITTEN IN THE STARS

Before the municipal era of vertical slums, boys who lived in the Auld Toon of Edinboro' or the Gallowgate of Aberdeen

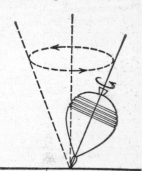

Fig. 10. The child's whipping top reproduces quite faithfully the precession and nutation in space of the earth's axis.

would bring their whipping tops out on to the pavement, each time that Candlemas came round again. They called their tops 'peeries', a term borrowed in the days of the 'Auld Alliance' from the French word 'pirouette'.

Fig 10 is a portrait of a typical peerie, nicely fashioned on a wood-turner's lathe, grooves for the whip and all. Flung outwards and downwards off the encircling cord of the whip, it lands on the pavement: and the odds are hundreds to one that its axis is inclined to the vertical when it starts to spin. It strives to spin upright, but has to compromise, at least for a start, by *precessing* about the vertical, and in so doing describes the so-called *space-cone*, whose apex coincides with the point of the top.

Moreover, it inevitably encounters transient side-pressures in the shape of bumps and hollows in the pavement, or of cracks between paving stones. These transients set up a *nutation* about the axis of the top itself whereby, precessing the while, the axis of rotation describes a *body-cone*, which rolls on the imaginary surface of the space-cone with a free period of nutation characteristic of the particular top in question. As time marches on, the *friction* between the point of the top and the pavement brings the axis of rotation into the vertical, in which position the friction is a minimum. The top sleeps – or in the vernacular 'snores'.

Here not for the first time the child is father of the man: for we have come to learn that our own earth is a top, spinning in space as it circles the sun, its axis of rotation precessing about the vertical to the plane of its orbit with a period of 26,000 years, sweeping out a cone in space having a semi-vertical angle of $23\frac{1}{2}°$. And because there is no friction on the point of a top spinning in space, that angle is held steady to all eternity.

The terrestrial top is forced into this precession by the torque which arises from the gravitational attraction of the sun and moon acting on the bulge of the earth at the Equator. But, just like the peerie, the earth's axis of rotation describes its own little body-cone in space, rolling on the space-cone as it precesses. This second motion of the earth's axis is a two-component 'free nutation', triggered by two separate mechanisms: first, a nutation having a period of 14 months, set off by the seasonal variation in the distribution of snow and ice, and of the atmosphere itself, between the northern and the southern hemispheres; and second a nutation having very nearly a diurnal period, triggered by the earth-tides in the crust and mantle. Let us look at these two periods of nutation, which together decide the angle of the body-cone, rather more closely.

To begin with, we recall that back in 1758 the great German mathematician, Euler, had analysed in complete detail the motions of a rigid spinning top; and proved that if the terrestrial top were a rigid body its period of free nutation should be 10 months. Then came S. C. Chandler of Cambridge (Massachusetts) who showed, from an analysis of the observed variations in the latitude of a number of places on the earth's surface over the period 1840 to 1891, that the period of free nutation of the terrestrial top was not 10, but 14 months. The reason is that the crust and mantle of the earth are *not* rigid. They possess *elastic properties*, as is evidenced above all in the phenomena of isostasy which we shall meet with later in Chapter 2.

And finally, in 1963, Nikolai Popov of the Poltava Gravimetrical Observatory in the Ukraine demonstrated that the free nutation having a near diurnal period arises from the spontaneous compression and decompression of *the earth's liquid core*, triggered off by the transient effect of the earth tides in its retaining shell.

Popov has established this very important fact as the result of a laborious observation of two bright stars in the zenith of the firmament – α Persei and η Ursa Major. Here he reverts in a measure to the methods of the Egyptian priest-scientists of the IVth Dynasty, who knew something of the precession, as distinct from the nutation, of the terrestrial top: for it is a fact that the sloping shafts of the Great Pyramid are most cunningly constructed so as to allow an exact observation by the dead Pharaoh of the star α Draconis, to which the earth's axis pointed 4,000 years ago, where today it points to our Pole Star, α in Ursa Minor. In like manner, beginning in 1933, Popov pointed his Zeiss zenith telescope, night and day for thirty years, alternately at η Ursa Major and α Persei as they replaced one another approximately every 12 hours at the zenith; and so determined the shorter period of free nutation as 23 hours 56 minutes 54 seconds, with the incredible accuracy of 4 parts in a thousand. And this is precisely the period predicted by his fellow-countryman Nikolai Pariinsky from his analysis of the triggering effect of the earth tides in crust and mantle on the free period of oscillation of a liquid nickel-iron core under compression.

And so the Soviet astronomers have corroborated the work of the Commonwealth seismologists; and we can be reasonably confident that the interior of the earth is indeed as depicted in our Fig. 2.

EARTH'S MANTLE

The density of the liquid iron core, as deduced from the speed at which the seismic waves radiating from earthquake centres travel in it, as also from Popov's new results, is about twice that of the surrounding mantle, which is most probably composed of iron-magnesium silicate rock, similar to the basaltic mineral olivine. When the interior of the earth first melted, core and mantle would have existed as a magma of liquid iron and iron silicates, from which the liquid iron gradually separated, much as in an industrial blast furnace: a process of separation which, as already stressed, is perhaps even yet not fully complete.

The mantle is the seat of the deep-focus earthquakes that tell us what we know of the interior of the earth; its outer zone is the source of the lavas that are the primordial constituent of continents and ocean islands; earth's volcanoes are the vents for the release of its volcanic gases, which metamorphosed give us the air we breathe; the seven seas were almost certainly once literally 'waters under the earth', hidden as 'juvenile water' in the mantle. In short, the mantle is of supreme importance in the shaping of earth's surface features: the mountains of the continental rafts; the coral atolls of the Pacific; the majestic topography of the ocean floor; even the overall pattern of land and sea – all have the stamp of the mantle upon them. Some of these products of the mantle are illustrated in Plates 2 and 3.

TRAVEL TIMES

Once the first bold outline of the mantle had been traced by the seismic waves from deep-focus earthquakes, the seismologists could proceed to a closer examination of its structure. Thus it is clear from a glance at Fig. 4 that the longer is the travel time between earthquake focus and observation station, the deeper is the level at which the seismic waves from that focus have had to make their way through the substance of the mantle. If then the substance of the mantle were uniform throughout its depth, the travel time would be uniformly proportional to the distance between the source of the earthquake and its point of detection at the earth's surface. However, it turns out that this is not the case.

In the first place, the travel times for waves that have passed through the lower levels of the mantle are found to be *less* than would be predicted from a constant proportionality between distance travelled in the mantle and travel time. In other words, the substance of the mantle near its boundary with the inner liquid core is *denser* than the average.

In the second place, the earlier workers found a distinct break in the uniform proportionality between travel time and distance travelled: namely, when source and seismograph were at an angular distance of some 20° apart, which came to be called in

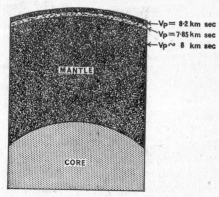

Fig. 11. Diagram illustrating the 'Gutenberg channel' in the upper mantle – a layer of lower rigidity and greater plasticity than the average, which allows the movement of extensive portions of the crust relative to each other and to the underlying mantle.

the jargon of seismology 'the 20° discontinuity'. In this case, however, the travel time was *greater* than the average: in other words, the velocity of propagation of seismic waves was *less* than the average.

The so-called '20° discontinuity' was analysed with particular care by the late Beno Gutenberg of Pasadena in California, on the basis of seismograph records of earthquakes originating in four different areas – Japan, the Mediterranean, Rumania and India. He expressed his results as indicating a layer in the upper mantle at a depth of between 100 and 200 kilometres below its upper boundary, in which the velocity of the P waves dropped from the customary 8·2 km/sec to 7·85 km/sec, and that of S waves from 4·6 km/sec to 4·4 km/sec: in short a layer in which the substance of the mantle is *less rigid and more plastic* than at levels either above or below it.

Gutenberg's conclusions, reached as the result of a laborious analysis of the travel times and amplitudes of seismic waves radiating from the foci of natural earthquakes, have been confirmed directly by the observation of these same quantities for seismic waves originating from underground explosions of atomic bombs in the Nevada desert. Quantitatively, the more precise delineation of the Gutenberg low-velocity layer made possible by such direct experiment gives the vertical span of the layer as between 60 and 150 km below surface.

Moreover, recent studies of *surface waves* from atomic explosions – seismic waves which travel in the crust but 'feel' the substrata to a depth of the same order as their own wavelength – show that the low-velocity layer is of global extent lying hidden beneath the surface of land and sea alike.

22 MAY 1960

Still, the 'Gutenberg channel' remained essentially in the realm of theoretical deduction until the Chile earthquake of 22 May 1960, which not only sent a great tidal wave sweeping across the Pacific to New Zealand and Japan, but also made the whole globe of the earth literally 'ring like a bell'. The fact that seismographs capable of directly recording the deep seismic notes of the earth's bell were already installed at two separate stations – at Isabella, California, and at Palisades, New York – is due primarily to Gutenberg's pupil, Hugo Benioff.

Benioff had detected an oscillatory movement with a period of over 50 minutes in the records of the Kamchatka earthquake of 4 November 1952, which he – rightly, as it turned out – attributed to a fundamental oscillation of the earth as a whole. Both he and Maurice Ewing of New York thereupon set out to build special long-period seismographs which could record precisely and directly such very long-period vibrations. At the same time, the theoreticians got busy with some highly complicated calculations, made possible only with the aid of modern high-speed electronic computers, which should predict not only the fundamental tone, but also the long series of overtones, which would fit the natural modes of five distinct earth models, including 'Bullen B' as modified for the upper mantle by Gutenberg.

So when the catastrophe of the Chile earthquake occurred, the coldly impersonal Benioff seismographs at Isabella and

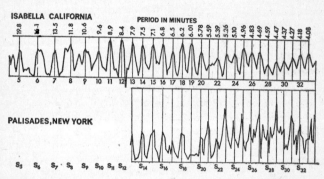

Fig. 12. The great Chile earthquake of 22 May 1960: overtones of the fundamental mode of vibration S1 of the earth as a spherical bell, observed simultaneously on the seismometers at Isabella, California, and Palisades, New York, compared with those predicted on the Bullen–Gutenberg model of the earth's interior. (After Benioff and Ewing.)

Palisades duly recorded the great bell of the earth ringing out the awful news: a deep fundamental vibration of period 53·9 minutes, and a whole series of overtones ranging from 19·8 minutes right up the scale of 32 steps to 4·08 minutes – and each and every one matched by the corresponding overtone predicted by the theoreticians *on the basis of the Bullen B model of the earth and the Gutenberg model of the upper mantle.*

Thus at a single stroke the actual existence of the thirty-year-old Gutenberg hypothesis of a layer of minimum rigidity and maximum plasticity in the upper portion of the mantle was established beyond a peradventure. Large-scale movements of portions of the earth's crust relative to the mantle, either vertically in the formation of continental rafts, or horizontally in continental drift or in transcurrent faulting of the ocean floor, the possibility of which has been so hotly debated in the past, now find their natural locus in the plastic Gutenberg channel: topics which are dealt with at length in succeeding chapters of this book.

THE EARTH'S CRUST

The primordial crust of the earth is a skin of magmatic basaltic rock some 5 miles thick, density around 3·0, lying atop the mantle to form both the ocean floor and the foundation of the continental rafts of granitic rocks, density approximately 2·6, themselves 20 to 25 miles in thickness.

That is a bald statement of the facts, as established by a study of shallow-focus or 'near' earthquakes on the one hand; and by 'seismic shooting' with man-made explosives, both on land and at sea, on the other.

Harold Jeffreys, in his classic book *The Earth*, says: 'Technically a near earthquake is one well observed at a number of stations near enough to record P and S waves in the granitic upper layer, that is, within about 6° (i.e., of earth's arc). It is usually a small earthquake, because in a large one at small distances the movement is too violent for anything but the first displacement to be read.'

Possibly the most fruitful of all near earthquakes occurred on the morning of 8 October 1909, about 40 kilometres south of Zagreb, where Dr Andrija Mohorovičić (pronounced Mohorro-vich-ich) was director of the meteorological observatory. Mohorovičić examined the seismograph records of the quake, not only those obtained at Zagreb, but others from stations all over Europe, and was led to the fundamentally important discovery of the 'Mohorovičić discontinuity' – an abrupt change in structure and material as between crust and underlying mantle.

The essence of Mohorovičić's discovery was the identification on his seismograph records of the arrival of not only one, but two P waves – the slower P wave having a velocity of about 6 km/sec, the faster one of 8·2 km/sec (see Plate 5). He boldly suggested that the slower P wave had followed the direct route from the focus of the near earthquake to his seismograph – that is, through the comparatively light-weight granites of the crust; while the faster P wave had travelled by refraction through the denser material of the upper mantle. On the basis of this hypothesis, he gave a first rough estimate of the thickness of the continental crust in the European area as 50 kilometres.

Mohorovičić's interpretation of his observations is now widely accepted, although quantitatively his figure of 50 kilometres for the crustal thickness was something of an over-estimate – 30

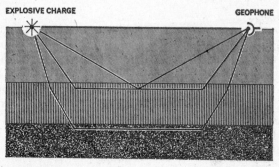

Fig. 13. 'Refraction shooting': the pressure wave from the explosive charge reaches the listening geophone by several possible routes – a direct wave travelling at the surface, a wave reflected at the first rock interface, and waves refracted both there and at lower interfaces.

to 45 kilometres, depending on the particular location, is now the currently accepted figure. However, 'Mohorovičić' has proved to be such a mouthful that his discontinuity – the boundary between crust and mantle – is universally known in the literature as 'the Moho'.

'Refraction shooting' with man-made explosives is now an accepted technique for the exploration of the earth's crust, particularly at sea. Here the experimenter has the obvious advantage of a precise knowledge of the time and place of his miniature earthquake. Usually the amount of explosive used is quite small – of the order of hundredweights rather than tons

– although isolated advantage has been taken to record the seismic waves sent out for example from the gigantic post-war explosion in 1947 of the ammunition dump on the island of Heligoland, or a year later in the underground war factory of Haslach in the Black Forest, or from the underground detonation of atomic bombs in the Nevada desert. All alike give the same answer – a crustal sheath of basaltic rock some 5 miles thick beneath land and sea alike, P wave velocity 6·7 km/sec, overlaid on land by a continental upper crust of granites, gneisses, and schists 20 to 25 miles in thickness, P wave velocity around 6 km/sec.

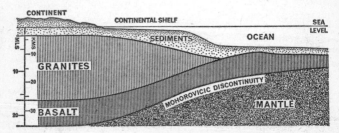

Fig. 14. A generalized picture of the structure of the earth's crust: a global sheath of basaltic rock, overlaid either by the sediments atop the ocean floor; or by the granitic rafts of the continents, floating like great icebergs in the substance of the mantle.

ISOSTASY

The basalt layer, which may well represent the earth's first primitive crust, must not be thought of as a geometrically perfect shell about the mantle, on which are piled the continents and the ocean sediments. Far from it. There are deep depressions in the floor of the oceans – the deep-sea trenches of a later chapter – below which the basalt layer is thinned out; while the same layer beneath the continents is buckled downwards, particularly below mountainous areas or beneath regions such as Greenland or Antarctica which are weighed down by an ice-cap. Under mountainous areas the basalt layer may either follow the profile of the peaks far above it, or may be so thickened that it actually offers a convex surface to the earth's interior; while the rise of the ground in areas such as Scandinavia, only recently released from the glaciation of the Pleistocene era, at the rate of a metre or more per century, is a well-established fact.

Such adjustments of the earth's crust are a consequence of 'isostasy', a term introduced by the American geologist Clarence Edward Dutton in 1892 to express the tendency of the crust towards *hydrostatic equilibrium*. The continents 'float' on the mantle, like icebergs in the sea; while the floors of the ocean trenches are sucked down into the mantle to lie submerged in it like sunken logs below the surface of a lake. A general impression of isostasy at work in maintaining the hydrostatic equilibrium of the crust is conveyed in Fig. 14.

LATERAL VARIATIONS IN THE PROPERTIES OF THE MANTLE

Five years ago few cared to inquire whether the substance of the mantle might show variations in breadth as well as in depth; in 1966, the dedicated followers of fashion among the seismologists could talk of little else.

The impetus to a systematic search for lateral inhomogenities in the upper mantle (defined as that part of it which lies above a depth of 1,000 km) came from the international Upper Mantle Project (UMP), initiated in 1960 by Viktor Beloussov (pronounced Bello-oo-zoff) of Moscow; and by mid-1966 the first fruits were already being garnered.

Take for example the Great Lakes Seismic Experiment, initiated at Lake Superior as a cooperative venture between Canadian and U.S. geophysicists. A series of underwater explosions were set off in the Lake, and the consequent seismic shocks observed at 56 different sites in Canada and the United States. On analysis, the seismograms gave an unequivocal account of marked lateral variations in the upper mantle lying beneath the ancient Canadian shield, with the boundary between crust and mantle changing from the shallowest ever observed in North America (less than 30 km) to the most unusual depth of nearly 60 km below the middle of the lake. Moreover, current gravity measurements could only be reconciled with this anomalous crustal thickness by admitting density differences in the upper mantle.

Advantage was taken of the heavy explosions in Lake Superior by the United States Geological Survey to construct a long refraction profile of crust and upper mantle extending as far to the south-west as Colorado. Remarkably enough, no trace of a low-velocity layer in the mantle could be seen on the records.

But the ripest plum is surely the one plucked by the U.S. Transcontinental Geophysical Survey, a picture of which you can see in Fig. 15. Briefly, it reveals two quite different, indeed idiosyncratic provinces in both crust and upper mantle beneath the United States, with a zone of demarcation between them defined by the Rocky Mountains. West of the Rockies, the *seismic profile* is characterized by a thin crust, and a low-velocity upper mantle; to the east, by a mature continental crust and normal upper mantle, marked by numerous intrusions of magma and lava flows. The *gravity profile* indicates that the western province is in detailed isostatic equilibrium; the eastern province, on the other hand, is characterized by large uncompensated loads. The *aeromagnetic survey* reveals an anomalous mantle in the western province, low in density and high in temperature; while the upper mantle of the eastern province is of normal density, and relatively cool.

These results are of prime importance in connexion with the underthrust of the North American continent by the East Pacific Rise, which is discussed at pp. 123-4 in Chapter 4.

DEEP DRILLING

The total thickness of the layer of sediments which lies sunk beneath some three miles of sea water atop the true ocean bottom is of the order of 1,000 feet; modern coring devices, although a big advance on the original Kullenberg piston corer shown in Fig. 34, can penetrate to perhaps one-tenth of that total. The basalt floor of the oceans is 4 to 5 miles in thickness; it has only been scratched in isolated spots. On land, the thickness of the

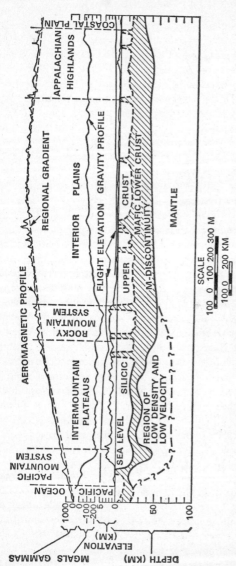

Fig. 15. The Transcontinental Geophysical Survey, coming within the U.S. programme of the Upper Mantle Project. The 'Regional gradient' is the smooth curve derived from the observed aeromagnetic profile, shown as a broken line; the term 'Gravity profile' needs no explanation; the 'Flight elevation' is the track followed by the aircraft carrying the magnetometers used in the aeromagnetic survey; 'Mafic' is the term used to describe the basic nature of the lower crust beneath the eastern geophysical province. The words 'Mgals' and 'Gammas' against the upper scale on the left refer to the gravity survey and the aeromagnetic survey respectively; $1\gamma = 1/1000$ gauss, where 1 gauss is the force exerted on unit magnetic pole; 1 gal $= 1$ cm/sec/sec. (After Pakiser and Zietz.)

granitic crust is 25 to 35 miles thick, the depth of the deepest oil well only about 5 miles.

Thus despite the undoubted power of the seismic method in probing the interior of the earth, our knowledge of its chemical composition and physical properties is at best inferential. Seeing is believing: hence the extensive programme of deep drilling within that of the Upper Mantle Project 1963–70.

Three chief categories of observations fall within the UMP deep-drilling programme: Heat-flow through the crust; the vertical distribution of the radio-elements which are incorporated in the rock strata of the continents; and finally the study of cores retrieved by boring into the ocean sediments – with a view to the better understanding of the history of the ocean basins, and of the earth's ancient climates.

Numerous measurements of the heat-flow through the ocean bottom in the Atlantic and Pacific alike (excluding the ocean ridges) give a mean value of 1.08 ± 0.054 microcalories/cm^2/sec. The much less reliable figure for heat-flow through the granitic continental crust lies somewhere between 1.1 and 1.5.

The *heat source* which is the origin of the flow of heat from the interior of the earth outwards we have already attributed to the radio-active elements entrapped in the cold material from which Proto-earth was formed by gravitational accretion; and a numerical check of the observed Uranium:Thorium content of meteorites from outer space against the calculated amount of radio-active material in the *continental* crust is indeed in tolerable agreement with the observed heat-flow.

Oceanic basalts, however, are only about one-third as radio-active as the continental granites and gneisses; and the question arises as to the origin of the heat-flow through the ocean floor. The only possibility would seem to be the physical intrusion from below of molten material from the upper mantle; and the high values of the heat-flow actually observed over the ocean ridges, and particularly over their spinal rift valley, amounting to 5 or 6 microcalories/cm^2/sec, is in good agreement with this hypothesis.

Later on, we shall link this deduction with the more general notion of convection currents in the mantle, with the demonstrable spreading of the ocean floor right and left of the ridges, and with the accumulating evidence for the reality of continental drift. Here we merely remark on the puzzling equality, or at least semi-equality of the heat-flow through the oceanic and continental regions of the crust.

It is for this latter reason that a concerted effort has been made to include as many thermal measurements as possible, and as many observations of the vertical distribution in the crust of Uranium and Thorium, within the framework of the UMP deep-drilling programme.

Cores taken from the ocean sediments are like ancient styles, on which is inscribed the history of the superficial layers of the adjacent lands, and of the marine fauna of successive geological epochs: telling on the one hand for example of glacial ebb and flow during the Quaternary; on the other of the surface temperature of the sea-water, and hence the ancient marine climate, in which the foraminifera whose fragile skeletons strewed the contemporary ocean floor lived and moved.

The 'geological thermometer' which Harold Urey, then of Chicago, developed in the early fifties depends on the preference which the foraminifera display for the heavier isotope of oxygen O^{18}, over that of ordinary oxygen-O^{16}, in building their calcareous skeletons of $CaCO_3$; coupled with the fact that the higher the temperature of the ambient water the less O^{18} is built into the molecules of the skeletal carbonates. In other words, the ratio of O^{18}/O^{16} in the organic carbonates of the foraminiferal skeletons entombed in a segment of a sediment core sample determines the paleo-temperature of the water in which the creatures lived.

So far, however, the length of core obtainable takes the temperature story only as far into the past as the late Tertiary (see Fig. 18); and although one may decipher thereon the succession of glacial epochs in the northern hemisphere which marked the recent Quaternary, one would like to read geological history right back to the Cretaceous period – the scene, as we shall see in Chapter 4, of certain remarkable events in the evolution of the earth's crust as we know it today.

The programme of deep drilling, as laid down within that of the Upper Mantle Project, was to have culminated in a bold enterprise: namely, in boring a hole clean through the ocean floor to below the Mohorovičić discontinuity, at a chosen site 170 miles out to sea off Honolulu. This was the politically notorious 'Project Mohole'.

But the summer of 1966 brought 'grief an' pain For promised joy'. The cruel ploughshare of a negative vote in the U.S. House and Senate strewed the winds with the needed $15 million and the leaves and stubble of lost hopes. Project Mohole was postponed indefinitely.

This was a pity. There was a finite hope that samples of the upper mantle in the geographical area of Hawaii might have been brought to the surface. There was the practical certainty that core-sampling of the total thickness of the sediments would have been achieved in the preliminary phases of the enterprise.

Moreover, the pilot experiment carried out in 1961 off the island of Guadalupe, which we illustrate in Plates 6 and 7, had gone extremely well. Valuable experience had been gained from this preliminary work in keeping a sea-going platform accurately positioned between four radar buoys securely moored to the ocean floor; in the prevention of possible fracture of the drill pipes in heavy seas by the use of a conical guide; in the retrieval of the cores by means of an inner tube held axially in the bottom section of the drill pipe; and so on. *CUSS I*, owned by the Continental, Union, Shell and Superior Oil Companies, did what was all in all a swell pioneer job.

CHAPTER TWO

Mountain Building

WHEN the liquid nickel-iron core separated out from the silicate rocks of the mantle, between 3,000 and 4,000 million years ago, the bulk of the radio-active elements, such as uranium and thorium, were left behind in the mantle. Too bulky to fit well into the crystal pattern of the constituents of the mantle, they began to work their way outwards towards the crust. Today the radio-active elements are concentrated mainly in the crust, possibly in the upper reaches of the mantle; but particularly in the granitic rocks of the continental rafts.

RADIO-ACTIVE CLOCKS

Now all radio-active substances decay, by the steady spontaneous disintegration of the nuclei of the atoms of which they are composed, into substances which are non-radio-active. The classic example is the decay of uranium, via a whole chain of radio-active elements, into the non-radio-active substance lead.

TABLE 1: Radio-active isotopes used in age determinations

Parent Isotope	End-product	Half-life (millions of years)
Uranium-238	Lead-206	4,510
Thorium-232	Lead-208	13,900
Potassium-40	Argon-40	11,850
	Calcium-40	1,470
Rubidium-87	Strontium-87	47,000

If then a sample of uranium-bearing rock is taken and analysed for the amount of lead end-product which has been produced from its parent, the age of the rock is determined from the known rate of decay of the uranium atoms.

In Table 1 are assembled a number of naturally occurring

radio-active substances, the clocks which are used to determine the age of the rocks forming the earth's crust.

Two definitions are needed in the study of this table. First, an 'isotope', as its name implies, is an elementary atomic species

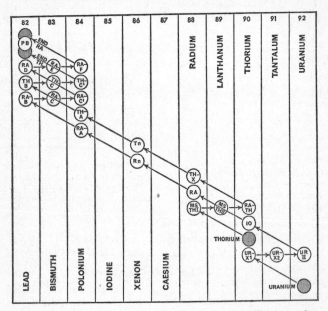

Fig. 16. The atomic disintegration series of Uranium and Thorium written across the face of the Periodic Table. Both series terminate in the birth of atoms of non-radio-active lead – atomic weight 206 for Uranium lead, 208 for Thorium lead ('ordinary' lead weighs 204 on the atomic weight scale). The numbers 82 to 92 are the so-called 'atomic numbers' of the elements, which begin with 1 for hydrogen. Look particularly at atomic number 84 – here there are as many as five atomic species isotopic with Polonium.

occupying the same place in the Periodic Table of the elements as one or more others. This becomes clear if for example we write the radio-active atomic disintegration series for Uranium and Thorium across the bottom of Mendeleef's Periodic Table of the chemical elements, as has been done in Fig. 16.

Second, the 'half-life' of a radio-active substance is the time taken for half the amount originally present to decay, through the spontaneous radio-active disintegration of its atomic nuclei, as is illustrated in Fig. 17.

A glance at Fig. 16 shows us that there are at least two species of lead, the non-radio-active end-products of the Uranium and

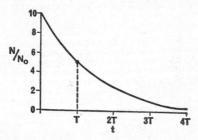

Fig. 17. The decay of a sample of a radio-active substance by spontaneous nuclear disintegration, illustrated graphically. N_0 is the number of atoms originally present in the sample; N is the number of atoms remaining un-transmuted after a lapse of time t; and T is the 'half-life', for which $N/N_0 = 0.5$.

Thorium disintegration series. Hence we are allowed at least two independent shots at determining the age of uranium- or thorium-bearing deposits, by analysing them with the aid of the mass spectrograph for the ratios U238:Pb206; and for Th232: Pb208 – since from measurements made in the laboratory we know the rate of decay and 'half-life' of the radio-active sub-stances U238 and Th232. A control is also available for the quantity of 'common' lead, not of radio-active origin, which may and usually is present in uranium-bearing pitch-blende or thorium-rich monazite sand, in the determination of the amount of Pb204 present, since this isotope of lead is not a product of the radio-active decay of heavier elements.

In this way, remarkably accurate determinations can be made of the age of a surprisingly large number of rocks. The scope of geological age determination has however been vastly increased in the past decade by the development of the two remaining methods featured in Table 1, namely the Argon-40: Potassium-40 method, and the Strontium-87: Rubidium-87 method, since

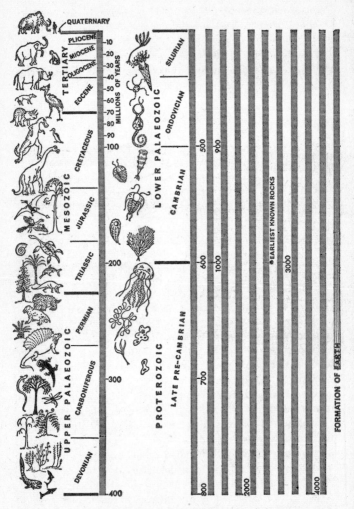

Fig. 18. The geological column of six eras and fourteen periods, the dates of which in the world's history book are recorded by radio-active clocks preserved in successive strata of the earth's crust.

Potassium-40 in particular is the constituent of many rock-forming minerals of all ages. Micas give particularly valuable results, since the volatile gas argon is held firmly in its atomic form in the natural crystal lattice.

And in Fig. 18 is the modern geological column which results, to which we shall frequently refer in the sequel.

THE OLDEST ROCKS

The age of the oldest rocks in the geological column as determined by radio-active dating, is around 3,000 million years – in excellent agreement incidentally with the astronomical estimate. These are the ancient continental nuclei, such as are found bare of overlying deposits of a later date in Canada south of Hudson Bay, north of the Black Sea in the Ukraine, south of the Deccan plateau in India, and in the gold-fields of Western Australia.

These primitive continental shields are made up of both sedimentary and volcanic rocks, with a high preponderance of volcanic types – pillow lavas and basalts – which are never found

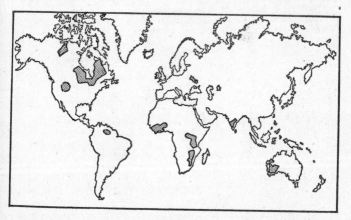

Fig. 19. The ancient continental shields of the Pre-Cambrian era. (After Tuzo Wilson.)

repeated on the same scale in later formations. How then shall we decipher the first chapter of geological history, the formation of the gigantic mountains of which the continental nuclei are the seventh age ? Perhaps the most fruitful approach to this problem is to look first with Tuzo Wilson of Toronto at the *youngest* mountains in the world – the islands arcs of the China seas.

ISLAND ARCS

Sp in a terrestrial globe so that you are faced with the Pacific Ocean, and you will see strung out before you, off the eastern shores of Asia, a long chain of islands, threaded like beads on a string from the Aleutians in the north to the island of Celebes in the south. Look closer, and observe that here is a necklace of *linked circular arcs*, concave towards the land, each one of them bordered on the seaward side by a deep trench in the ocean floor: the Aleutian trench, the Kuril trench, the Japanese trench, the Philippine trench.

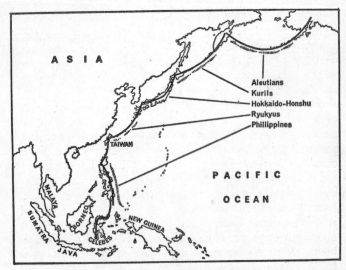

Fig. 20. Island arcs and trenches in the China Seas.

These abyssal trenches of the Pacific are deep gashes in the earth's crust, their depth having numerical values clustered closely about an average of 35,000 feet, the floor of their V-shaped canyons devoid of any form of sediment. The deepest of them, the Marianas trench, has been sounded by the USSR oceanographic vessel *Vitiaz* at 36,173 feet – deeper than Mount Everest is high. Gravity surveys, made by swinging a pendulum in an ocean-going submarine navigating the dead calm waters beneath the waves, reveal very large 'negative anomalies' beneath such trenches. In other words, the force of gravity is here way below its average value, which can only mean that the floors of the trenches lie far beneath the average level of the earth's crust – as if they had been sucked down under lateral compression into the substance of the upper mantle, dragging crustal material and ocean-bottom sediments alike into the mantle below.

Now seismic shooting between two vessels at sea has shown that the ocean floor underneath the trenches is thinned out to a thickness less than the average value of 5 to 10 miles. And earthquake studies tell us that below the floor of every trench are the foci of shallow-intermediate earthquakes originating in the uppermost region of the mantle. Follow these shallow foci downwards, and you find not only shallow but deep earthquake foci, all lying on the surface of a cone of semi-vertical angle 45° whose apex lies 400 miles or more below the earth's surface. Moreover, such observational data are confirmed by a theoretical analysis of the fracture of a crust under compression, lying above a mantle in tension: an analysis which leads to just such a conical zone of fracture as would result in the formation of an arctuate ocean trench where the cone cuts the surface. (See Fig. 22.)

The island arcs which lie shoreward of the trenches are invariably volcanic in origin: they are formed of so-called *andesitic* lavas; lavas, that is, which carry a relatively high content of silica, in contrast to the purely basaltic lavas of which isolated mid-ocean islands are formed. Here the lavas of the island arcs betray their sub-continental origin: they have come upwards from the mantle through the continental crust to find the zone of crustal fracture defined by the trenches. In fact the whole surface

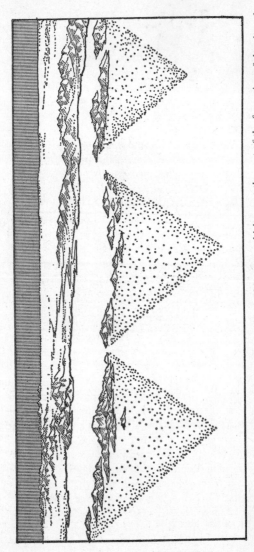

Fig. 21. Perspective view of cones of fracture in the earth's crust, which are at the root of the formation of the abyssal trenches, and shoreward of these the volcanic island-arcs.

geology of the Pacific basin is governed by the so-called *andesite line*, shoreward of which the lavas are of the continental type, a line which follows closely the seaward boundary of the chain of island arcs.

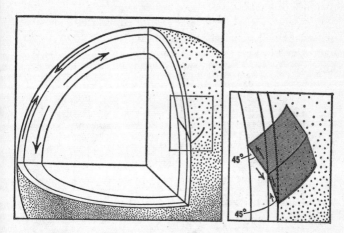

Fig. 22. Diagram showing how compressional stresses in the earth's crust, above an upper mantle under tensional stress, lead by faulting to arctuate splits in the crust. (After Scheidegger.)

WORLD-WIDE FRACTURE ZONE

Follow now the line of island arcs you have looked at in the China Seas right around the globe. First, note that the chain branches at the island of Celebes: one branch thrusts eastward via New Guinea to the Solomon Islands, the New Hebrides and the North Island of New Zealand; while the other swings westward via the Java trench, then northwards with the newly discovered Andaman Trench (in 1963, by *Pioneer*, U.S. Coast and Geodetic Survey research vessel) to come ashore as the convex western aspect of the Burma Range; then via the majestic ex-island arc of the Himalayas westward to the mountain arcs of Persia and of Turkey; and thence to the Dolomites of the Adriatic and the Apennines of Italy.

Next, retrace your steps northward from Celebes, up past the Philippines, Japan, the Kurils, the Aleutians: then over the top of the world to Alaska, and away south along the coastal mountains of British Columbia and the United States to the Andes of South America.

You have traced out on your globe a gigantic letter T, which marks the line along which splits in the earth's crust have occurred or indeed are still being made, to form a world-wide compressional zone of linked conical fractures.

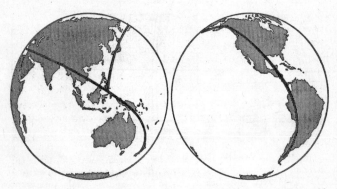

Fig. 23. The great T which the zone of compressional fracture in the earth's crust traces on the globe.

AGE GROUPS

The arctuate formations which together form the great compressional fracture zone of the earth's crust are not all of the same age – far from it. Thus for example the island arcs of the China seas are about 150 million years of age, the Andes 250 million years, the Sierra Nevada and Cascade mountains of the western United States 400 million years; and once this difference in age among the different systems of mountain arcs is appreciated, the idea of an *evolutionary process* at work in mountain building becomes clamant.

Thus in the single island arcs of the Pacific we are witnessing the primary stage of mountain building at a continental margin;

in the Andes we see the full formation of a primary mountain arc, as part of its continent; while the Sierra Nevada/Cascade mountain chain is one member of a double mountain arc, the other being the Coastal Range of the western United States.

DOUBLE MOUNTAIN ARCS

The formation of a double mountain arc is the natural consequence of the initial juxtaposition of island arc and ocean trench. With the passage of time, the trench is gradually filled with sediments arising from the erosion of the volcanic peaks of the island arc; then comes the upthrust of the crust seaward required to maintain the overall balance of the load on the underlying mantle.

There are many examples of such double mountain arcs, apart from the Sierra Nevada/Coastal Range system in the United States – above all, in the series of five double arcs stretching westwards from Celebes on the east-west arm of 'the

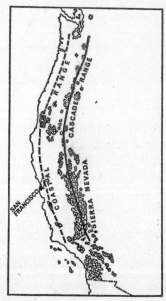

Fig. 24. The Sierra Nevada and Coastal Range of California: an example of the formation of a double mountain arc. (After Tuzo Wilson.)

great T'. Of these again, the most dramatic is the Himalayan double arc, facing south to the Indian subcontinent – where in pre-Cretaceous times there rolled the ancient Tethys Sea.

SECONDARY MOUNTAIN ARCS

Pinpointing once again the Sierra Nevada and the Cascade Mountains, together with the British Columbian coastal mountains lying to the north, we observe that they form a two-

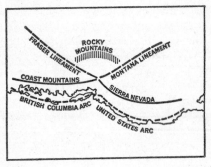

Fig. 25. An example of the formation of a secondary mountain arc. (After Tuzo Wilson.)

linked chain of circular arcs, with their *convex* aspect towards the coast; and further, that opposite the junction of these two arcs lies the curved bow of the Rocky Mountains, some two hundred miles inland, presenting its *concave* aspect to the coast.

Here in the Rockies is a typical example of a *secondary mountain arc*, thrown up by faulting in the cover rocks lying inland of the primary arcs: faults or 'lineaments' which spring from the area of stress in the crust where two conical fractures meet. Of the many other secondary arcs bordering 'the great T' we mention the Alps, the Caucasus, the Pamirs, and the mountains of the Burma Road: all formed on the continental side of the junctions between the five great primary arcs of the east-west fracture zone stretching from Celebes to the Strait of Gibraltar, and all with their concave faces looking south; or rather less dramatically, in the Puna Ridge of Bolivia, inland

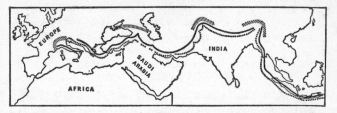

Fig. 26. The festoon of primary and secondary mountain arcs which hangs on the east-west arm of the great T. (After Tuzo Wilson.)

from the Andes and again concave to the coast; or in the embryonic secondary arcs of Western Kamchatka, the south island of Japan, and of Formosa – children of the youngest of all primary arcs, the island arcs of the China Seas.

ACTIVE AND INACTIVE

All the mountain ranges so far considered are classed as 'active', a term which includes the active volcanoes of the East Asian island arcs, the earthquake belt of the Andes, the all but quiescent Sierra Nevada, the still upthrusting mountains of the southern Eurasian belt. As inactive are classed such mountain systems as the great Appalachian system of North America; the still older Laurentian mountains in Canada, the Scottish Grampians, the Scandinavian shield; and of course the primeval continental nuclei.

Can we then trace on their wrinkled faces the heyday of a youth spent as an active mountain arc? The answer is: Yes, if we look closely enough.

THE APPALACHIANS

The Appalachians, the major mountain system of the eastern United States, are a prime example of an inactive mountain range of comparatively recent age. Their rocks date from Palaeozoic times, around 400 million years ago, as compared with the oldest rocks of the Pre-Cambrian era, aged some 3,000 million years. Yet they are quite inactive, in the sense that both volcanism and earthquakes are completely absent; and one asks oneself immediately whether there is any evidence that they once formed part of a system of active mountain arcs: in other words, whether they represent today a later stage than say the Andes in an evolutionary process of mountain building and continental growth.

Now the earliest systematic survey of the geology of the United States traced a narrow chain of seven linked 'salients' in the Appalachian complex – in Newfoundland, in the Gaspé Peninsula, in Quebec Province; in Pennsylvania, Tennessee, Oklahoma and Texas: *and all thrusting inland with their concave aspect towards the coast.* Thus with the analogy of the Rocky

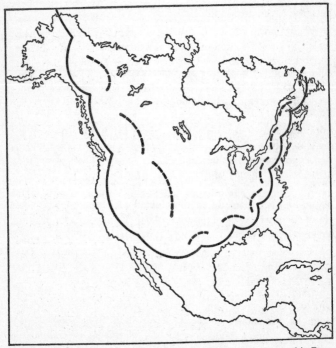

Fig. 27. The Appalachian mountain system as it may have appeared in Pre-Cretaceous times. (After Tuzo Wilson.)

Mountains in their relation to the Sierra Nevada and the Coastal Mountains of British Columbia as guide, the geologists searched seawards from the junctions between the salients, presumed to be *secondary* arcs, for the faults which would lead them to the junctions of the *primary* arc system, should such exist. Five of these fault lines have in fact been identified, two in the north and three in the south; and traces of a sixth have been detected in the New York area, buried beneath a subsequent deposit of sedimentary rocks.

Next comes the search for remnants of the primary arcs which should lie between consecutive pairs of seaward-trending fault lines: and sure enough, the appropriate volcanic rocks are found cropping out across Newfoundland, Nova Scotia, New Brunswick, New England, and inland from the coastal plain which lies north of Florida and the Gulf of Mexico. Moreover, traces of the sedimentary rocks of the outer member of a double mountain arc system have been identified in Newfoundland and Nova Scotia in the north, and in Virginia and the Carolinas in the south.

All these rocks, volcanic and sedimentary alike, date from the Carboniferous period; and the evidence is therefore reasonably complete that the Appalachians were at that time a seven-fold system of active mountain arcs. But here comes a new conundrum: for the threefold system of mountain arcs, active at the present day, which lie on the western seaboard of the North American continent – namely, the British Columbian, United States, and Mexican arcs – dates from the same Carboniferous period as the Appalachians. It looks indeed as if the whole North American continent had in the Carboniferous period been girdled with a complete ring of mountain arcs, ten in number, and that in post-Carboniferous times the main fracture zone of the earth's crust had switched its direction through a complete right angle: that instead of swinging east from the Mexican arc into the Appalachian system, it thrust south to the Andes, leaving the Appalachians to die of an early old age. We shall return to this most interesting and subtle question in Chapter 4.

THE OLDEST FORMATIONS

North of the Appalachians are the remnants of two mountain ranges whose rocks are the oldest in the world: namely the Laurentian shield, and that of the Keewatin province, lying respectively east and south of Hudson Bay in Canada, the one 1,000 million years old, the other aged 2,500 million years.

Yet even here faint traces of arctuate structure can be found imprinted on the surface rocks; although erosion, subsequent uplift to re-establish isostatic equilibrium, further erosion, and moreover massive glaciation, have obliterated all but the deepest basins of the original arcs. And there is a striking difference between them: the lavas of the Laurentian system are andesitic, the pillow lavas of the Keewatin province are basaltic, like the isolated volcanic islands of the Pacific.

Thus it would appear that the basaltic rocks of Keewatin were formed by volcanic action through the primitive crust of the earth, the five-mile basaltic layer which as we have already seen forms at once the ocean floor and the basement of the

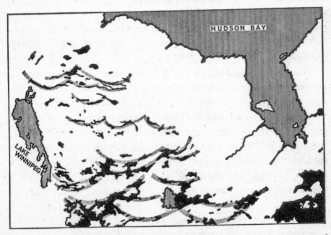

Fig. 28. The exposed face of the Pre-Cambrian shield in the province of Keewatin in Canada, on which traces of the ancient wrinkles left by its 3,000-million-year-old arcs can still be discerned.

continents. Subsequently, around 2,000 million years ago, the character of the continental rocks changed from highly basic to preponderantly acidic – examples of this transition being found for instance in the Finno-Scandinavian shield, aged 1,800 million years.

CONTINENTAL GROWTH

Having traced the formation of the world's mountain systems back from the youngest island arcs of the Pacific to the ancient continental nuclei, it remains to make a survey in the opposite direction in time, namely from the oldest to the youngest. Thus 2,500 million years ago came the first volcanoes, closely parallel lines of basaltic peaks marking the first conical fractures of the upper mantle and crust; 2,000 million years ago came the change in the character of the lavas belched out through the cracks in the crust, from basaltic to andesitic, marking the first stage of continental growth – the accumulation of the metamorphosed sediments originating from aerial erosion of the first andesitic volcanic peaks, of which the shields of eastern Canada and of Scandinavia are the scarred remnants; 1,000 million years ago saw yet another outburst of mountain building; and from 200 to 500 million years ago occurred the formation of the mountain arcs seaward of the older formations which can be clearly recognized as such today.

This idea of four distinct periods of mountain building is in keeping with the remarkable results of the recent surveys of data on the radio-active dating of igneous and metamorphic rocks, such as accumulate during the formation of active mountain arcs. These surveys indicate that mountain building has occurred in the past in quite well-defined spurts: for the ages of the rocks examined fall into four well-defined groups centred on the dates of 200 million, 1,000 million, 1,800 million and 2,600 million years ago.

SLIPWAY FOR CONTINENTS

A final loose end needs to be tied up in this story of mountain building from the substance of the mantle: namely to demonstrate that the rate of emission of lava from all the volcanoes of the world over a period of 3,000 million years is sufficient to account for the total bulk of all the continents, which amounts to some 6,000 million cubic kilometres.

Now five hundred volcanoes in all are known to have been active in historical times, with an estimated total emission of 320 cubic kilometres of lava since A.D. 1500. This is equivalent to an average rate of emission of just on one cubic kilometre per annum. Allowing then for the higher than average volcanism evidenced by the older rocks, a total emission since the first Pre-Cambrian eruptions of the required 6,000 million cubic kilometres of lava is not unreasonable.

So an answer can now be given to the question posed earlier (p. 60): How shall we interpret the first chapter of geological history, the formation of the gigantic mountains of which the continental shields are the seventh age? The answer is quite simply that all the mountains in the world, all the great continental rafts of the earth's crust, have been launched from the upper mantle along the slipways of conical fracture, in at least four distinct outbursts of volcanic action, marking as many stages in the formation of the continents from the first basaltic nuclei of 2,500 million years ago.

CHAPTER THREE

The Ocean Floor

IF the oceans could be drained of their five million million cubic feet of water, what would a spying satellite see as it circumnavigated the globe?

It would see the floor of the Arctic Ocean divided into three deep basins, ten thousand feet or more below continental level. It would see the coastal mountains of Greenland as a sort of pie-crust around the deep hollow in the earth's surface sculpted by the weight of the ice cap. It would see a gigantic range of mountains running plumb down the middle of the Atlantic, torn throughout its length of 10,000 miles by a great rift valley, 6,000 feet deep and thirty miles wide. It would see the highest cliffs in the world, a sheer plunge of 20,000 feet, north of the Falkland Islands. Antarctica would come into view as part continent, part archipelago. The Atlantic Ridge would be seen swinging round the Cape of Good Hope into the West Indian Ocean. Our satellite would see the Pacific Ocean girdled on the west with a string of island arcs and chasmic trenches; the floor of the ocean studded with hundreds of volcanic sea-mounts; to the east the great hump of the East Pacific Rise. It would see the great faults in the sea bed off the western coast of North America, swinging away from the San Andreas fault on land.

This detailed knowledge of the bottom of the sea has been won during the past forty years from the increasingly systematic use of a single observational method – that of *echo-sounding*.

The echo-sounder is a sword which has been beaten into a ploughshare – or maybe in this case into Neptune's trident: for it began away back in the First World War, the brainchild of Pierre Langevin of France and Ernest Rutherford of England, as a weapon against the German U-boats.

Langevin and Rutherford's line of reasoning was this: 'We've all had our fun in listening to the echo of a shout sent back from cliff or corrie; and we've all recognized the fact that the further away the reflecting surface the longer we have to wait for the echo. Send out a short pulse of supersonic vibration from a destroyer or "Q-ship", and if you get an echo back it's a U-boat.'

And now for Neptune's trident, first used to good purpose in 1925 by the German oceanographic vessel *Meteor* (Plate 9) in her exploration of the Atlantic sea-bed. The idea is this: Built into

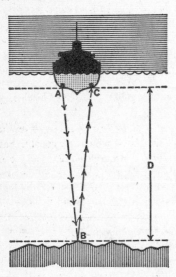

Fig. 29. A simple form of echo-sounder, still in use by, for example, trawl fishermen in their search for herring shoals, or to guide them on their way as they traverse the shallows above the banks. The 'ping' sent out from the supersonic transmitter A is reflected by the sea-bed at B; the 'pong' of the echo is reported by the receiver C. The time which has elapsed between 'ping' and 'pong' tells the navigator the depth D of the sea-bed below the keel of his boat.

the keel of the ship are a supersonic transmitter, as also a supersonic receiver tuned to the same frequency. The transmitter and receiver alike are short cylinders of a special magnetic alloy, which has the property of contracting spasmically when given a magnetic shock from a sudden surge of current in the coil surrounding it. Thus the transmitting cylinder goes 'ping'. The identical receiver 'listens' for the 'pong' echoing back from the sea bottom, 'hears' it, contracts, and sends an induced electric current through its coil to the receiving stylus, which has already marked the instant of the 'ping' on a revolving drum. The velocity of sound in sea-water is known; and the time interval which has elapsed between signal and response gives you the depth below surface of the sea bottom.

From these primitive beginnings has grown up a whole new technology of echo-sounding. Tens of thousands of miles of underwater profiles lying beneath the tracks of ocean-going vessels have been logged. The relative accuracy of the depths recorded has steadily increased until, with a sophisticated modern apparatus such as you see in Plate 10, the ups and downs in the ocean floor below the ship's track can be read off with an accuracy of 1 in 3,000. Note however that here 'accuracy' really means 'relative accuracy': for the *absolute* accuracy depends on the value taken for the velocity of sound in an idealized 'sea-water', water which can in practice vary in density, salinity, and temperature from one location to another over the enormous expanse of the world ocean, within considerably wider limits than 1 in 3,000.

Thus the *bathymetric charts* – maps of the ocean floor, in other words, such as that of Plate 11 – which are constructed from the logs of the ships' tracks, are accurate in *absolute* depth to not more than say 1 in 500. Nevertheless, here is a navigational aid of the future. Already ocean-going submarines like the *Nautilus* can find their way around from the very special information supplied to them by their governments about the topography of the ocean floor; and the day may not be so far distant when *all* ocean-going vessels are free to navigate the high seas by echo-sounding rather than by the stars. And indeed already the trawler skippers out of little fishing ports in the county of Caithness in northern Scotland are using their echo-sounders as much to find their way home in fog as to search for the 'silver darlings'.

But what of the seascape revealed by the magic box of the echo-sounder? Already we have seen that it is no flat featureless plain such as was predicated in the old school-books. Instead, the modern oceanographer recognizes at least six phases of ocean-bottom topography – the continental shelf, the continental slope, the abyssal plains; the mid-ocean ridges, the submerged sea-mounts of the Pacific, those deep ocean trenches which play such a big part in mountain building, all of which are illustrated in Fig. 30. Ocean trenches have been discussed already in Chapter 2; let us now survey the other five features one by one.

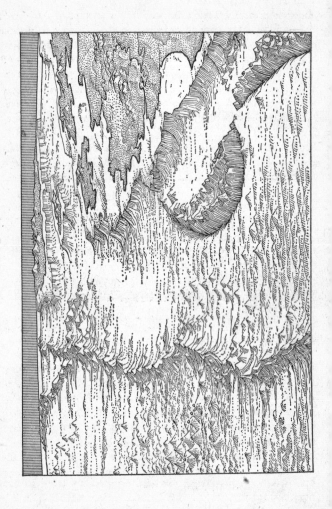

CONTINENTAL SHELVES

Every continental land mass on the globe thrusts itself into at least one of its surrounding oceans as a submerged *continental shelf* – a gradually sloping platform of shallow seas, with a width varying from a few miles off Monaco in the Mediterranean, or off the Island of Bermuda in the western Atlantic, to a hundred miles or more off the Arctic border of northern Asia.

Now you may still read in school textbooks of Physical Geography that the shallow seas are the product of aeons of wave action on the margins of the continents: in other words, that the continental shelves are the result of *sea erosion*. In such books the inner stretches of the shelves are erroneously classified as *wave-cut terraces*, supposed to be gnawed out of the

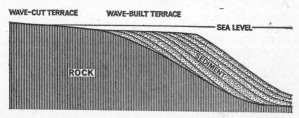

Fig. 31. The false picture of the origin of the continental shelves, as being the work of sea waves rather than that of aerial and glacial erosion: still propagated in some of the more backward schools and colleges. (After Shephard.)

continental shores by the ocean breakers. The outer margins of the shelves are pictured as *wave-built terraces*, deposits of silt and sediment cast up by the waves or deposited by rivers. The margin of the shelves is referred to as *the wave base*, because seawards of the shelf all wave action is assumed to have ceased.

This tired old stuff has in the past few decades been ruth-

Fig. 30. An artist's impression of the floor of an ocean that exists only in his imagination. It shows all the ocean-bottom features in a single picture: the continental land mass, the continental shelf, the continental slope, the abyssal plains, a mid-ocean ridge, and the volcanic islands and island arcs and trenches characteristic of the Pacific.

lessly scrapped by the modern echo-sounder, the under-water camera, the oil drill and the aqualung diver: and four chief reasons can now be advanced against the idea of a wave-born continental shelf.

First, the echo-sounder has revealed that the substratum of the shelf, right out to the edge of the continental slope, is solid rock, even where it is covered by sediments deposited off the mouths of the great rivers. Second, these same sediments are so variable in grain size, indeed almost capriciously so, that they couldn't possibly have been laid down by the ocean waves, which deposit their coarser burden first, their finer-grained cargo nearer in-shore. Third, the depth of the outer margins of the shelf bears no relation whatsoever to the prevailing size of the waves beating upon them. And fourth, the topography of the shelf is at times that of hill country on land, as is beautifully illustrated in Plate 12.

The complex picture of the continental shelves of the world delineated by modern methods is in marked contrast to the simple old sketch of the standardized wave-cut terrace. In the first place, there is the sharp difference in the width of the shelf in the Atlantic and Pacific basins. On the whole, the shelf off the continental margins of the Pacific is much narrower than those of the Atlantic, or may even be lacking altogether: for the Pacific Ocean is bordered chiefly by young island arcs and trenches which do not yet allow of the formation of large river systems, depositing the products of erosion on the sea-bed; in any case not in the time available since their birth. In the Atlantic, it is true that narrow shelves occur off the coast of Florida and Cape Hatteras: but here the absence of a wide shelf is due to the scouring action of the Gulf Stream, sweeping northwards at the rate of three or four miles an hour.

Wide continental shelves occur all over the world seaward of the mouths of large rivers: off the northern coast of Siberia, off the mouth of the Amazon, in the Persian Gulf, in the Bay of Bengal. In seas with the right temperature and salinity, as off the coast of Queensland in Australia, coral growth can lead to an exceptionally wide shelf.

GLACIATION OF THE SHELF

On both sides of the North Atlantic, the continental shelves appear to have been carved mainly by the action of glaciers. Twenty thousand years ago the Arctic Ocean was in all probability an open sea. The resultant precipitation in the northern hemisphere of snow pre-cooled by the low-temperature radiation from the ice-free arctic water surface would pack to glacial ice over the land and around the coasts. An ever-increasing amount of water would be taken from the sea and deposited on land, until finally all communication between the Atlantic and Arctic Oceans over the Arctic sill would be cut off. Thereafter, the Arctic Ocean would freeze, precipitation would decrease, the glaciers would retreat, sea-level would rise, until once again warm Atlantic water would have free access to the Arctic basin: and the cycle would repeat itself. At the present time, we may be fast approaching another phase of ice-free waters around the pole – and a repetition within the next 10,000 years of the Pleistocene ice-age.

At the height of the Pleistocene ice-age, sea-level would have been not less than 100 metres below its present value. Thus the whole of the Atlantic continental shelf would have been exposed to ice action. Evidence of such action is indeed to be found to this day: in glacial debris off the Norwegian coast, in the fishing banks of Newfoundland and the North Sea, in the numerous shallow basins which are equivalent to the lakes gouged out by glacial action on land – and, often hidden by the subsequent deposit of sediments, genuine wave-cut terraces at the margin of the shelf.

Summing up: the continental shelves have been formed, not by sea erosion, but *by deposition* – either by rivers, or by coral growth; and eroded by the winds and by glacial action at a period of low sea-level. Narrow shelves are found either seaward of young mountain arcs, or where fast currents move parallel to the shore.

CONTINENTAL SLOPES

The continental shelf ends abruptly, at an average depth of 300 feet, in a steep slope. The gentle gradient of the shelf, of

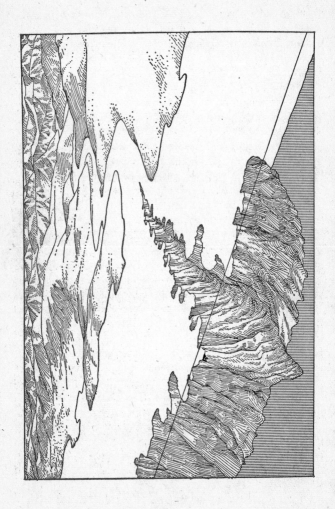

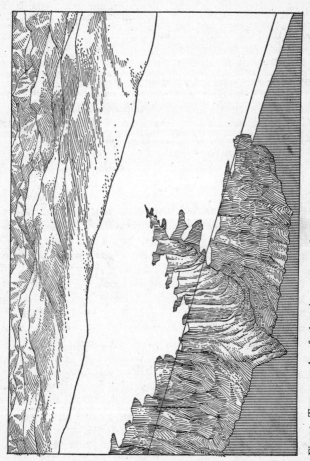

Fig. 32. Two examples of submarine canyons: the one an integral part of the topography of a river estuary, the other having no connexion with any topographical feature on land.

perhaps 1 in 500, up which it would be quite easy to ride a bike, increases within a mile or so to perhaps 1 in 4, which would tax a tank.

The *continental slopes* mark the true boundaries of the land masses, and they do so in no uncertain fashion in their plunge to the true ocean depths. Thus for example the foot of the escarpment off the west coast of South America is 42,000 feet below the tops of the Andes, that is almost twice the height of the southern aspect of the Himalayas; while a drop of 10,000 feet is quite commonly to be found. Usually the slope is continuous between the margin of the continental shelf and the deep sea floor; occasionally, however, you find an intermediate terrace, as for example off the coast of Florida, or even a series of basins and hills, as off the coast of California.

A feature common to almost all continental slopes is the presence of *deep-sea canyons*, steep-sided gashes in the slope that at times rival the Grand Canyon on land in both length and depth. Sometimes these submerged canyons are quite clearly the continuation of the continental river valleys, like the Hudson Canyon off New York or the Congo Canyon off the west coast of Africa. But far more often they bear no relation whatsoever to the adjacent continental river topography.

The origin of these awe-inspiring submarine canyons, first observed at the beginning of the present century, was hotly debated for upwards of fifty years. The preferred hypothesis over this period was that they arose from glacial action in Pleistocene times, although Kuenen of Groningen in Holland had demonstrated by laboratory models that they could be reproduced in all their characteristic features by turbidity currents – turbulent streams of water carrying solids in suspension.

The matter was clinched in favour of Kuenen's turbidity currents in 1952, when Bruce Heezen and Maurice Ewing of Columbia, New York, published their celebrated 'Who-dun-it' on the destruction of the submarine cables off the Grand Banks of Newfoundland on 18 November 1929.

To quote from Jacobs, Russell and Wilson's *Physics and Geology*:

Fig. 33. The Newfoundland Grand Banks turbidity current of 18 November 1929, triggered by an earthquake on the edge of the continental shelf, which fractured successively six and then three cables (in all nine) as it tore its way down the continental shelf. (After Heezen and Ewing.)

On 18 November 1929, at 2032 G.M.T., a severe earthquake of magnitude 7·2 shook the continental shelf and continental slope south of Newfoundland. The epicenter lay beneath the continental slope where it is at a depth of between 2000 and 4000 m in a region crossed by many trans-Atlantic cables. The six cables closest to the epicenter were broken immediately, but cables at successively greater distances in increasingly deeper water for 500 km south of the epicenter were in turn broken during the following 13 hr, 17 min after the quake. On the other hand, none of those lying nearby to the north on the continental shelf were disturbed. Repair ships found that sections of the broken cables were removed or buried over an area which was 600 km long and narrow in the north but 500 km broad in the south. Half of the breaks occurred on the ocean floor at the foot of the continental slopes in places where the gradient is less than 1°.

Heezen and Ewing showed that the above observations could be explained as the result of a great flow of muddy water – in fact a turbidity current – initiated by mud slumping near the epicenter and subsequently being diluted by mixing with water. The intervals between interruptions of messages in different cables showed that the current had reached a velocity of over 100 km/hr on the continental slopes and that it had progressively lost speed. Cores taken later showed that a graded bed averaging 1 m in thickness had been deposited over an area of 200,000 km² and that the flow had traveled for over 1000 km from the epicenter.

Since the date of Heezen and Ewing's important discovery, upwards of thirty contemporary turbidity currents, ripping down their submarine canyons with a freight of stones and silt from the continental shelf, have been recognized: which finally makes nonsense of the glacial-action theories. Moreover, the recording of these turbidity currents has shown that their erosive action in the great sunken canyons is *sporadic* – quite like that of the water which progressively gouges out the wadis of the Indian desert during each season of the monsoon rains (see Plate 13).

THE ABYSSAL PLAINS

Next, the *abyssal plains*, discovered as late as 1947 by the *Atlantis* (Plate 9) out of Woods Hole, New England: stretches of featureless sediment which even the eye of the under-water camera of

Plate 14 sees as completely smooth. Actually, they are misnamed. They are not completely flat. They tail into the continental slope quite regularly and continuously, with a gradient that begins seaward at say 1 in 2,000, to finish with perhaps 1 in 500 at the foot of the slope in the so-called 'continental rise'. They are most probably formed from the detritus torn from the continental shelf by turbidity currents which, laden with rocks and sediment, come roaring over the edge of the shelf to deposit their load at the foot of the slope, coarser material first, the finest-grained silt last: obliterating completely the rough topography of the true ocean floor.

There is indeed a marked contrast between the sediments recovered by modern coring devices from the surface of the abyssal plains and those from the adjacent continental rise. The former consist essentially of shallow water quartz sands, grey clays and silts, such as would be carried seawards by turbidity currents originating at the edge of the continental shelf: the latter almost entirely of the calcareous skeletons of the so-called zooplankton of the surface waters of the ocean – delicate little foraminifera whose exquisitely formed bones drift down through hundreds of fathoms of sea-water to rest in the ooze covering the continental rise and the lower slopes of the mid-ocean mountains.

The thickness of the deep ocean sediments in both the Atlantic and Pacific Oceans has been measured in scores of places by seismic methods, the average thickness being about 2,000 feet in the Atlantic and 1,000 feet in the Pacific. These figures are wildly at variance with estimates based on the amount of silt carried oceanwards by all the rivers of the world over the whole of geological time, which give an average thickness for the deep sea sediments of approximately *two miles*. We shall return to this discrepancy in the next chapter.

MID-OCEAN MOUNTAINS

Plumb down the middle of the Atlantic Ocean runs a majestic range of submerged mountains – the Mid-Atlantic Ridge. No mountain range on land can compare with it, not only in

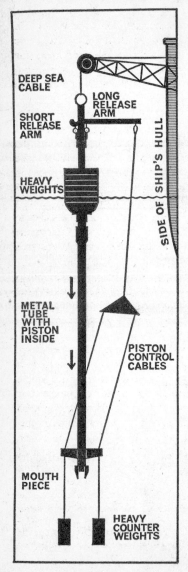

DEEP SEA
CABLE

LONG
RELEASE
ARM

SHORT
RELEASE
ARM

SIDE OF SHIP'S HULL

HEAVY
WEIGHTS

METAL
TUBE
WITH
PISTON
INSIDE

PISTON
CONTROL
CABLES

MOUTH
PIECE

HEAVY
COUNTER
WEIGHTS

a

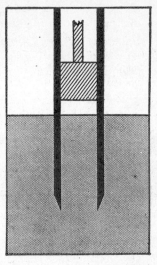

b

Fig. 34. The piston corer in the primitive form so successfully exploited by its inventor, Bjorge Kullenberg of Gothenburg in Sweden. The principle on which the Kullenberg corer and its more elaborate successors work is clearly shown in *a*. The corer, weighted for penetration into the ocean sediments, is lowered over the side of the mother ship counterpoised by two heavy weights which dangle below it as it descends through the superjacent water. The counterweights strike bottom first, thereby tripping the long/short-arm lever above. The weighted core tube plummets vertically to the ocean bottom, and penetrates the surface of the sediments. The piston shown in *b* now comes into operation: it abhors the vacuum which the continued descent of its cylinder tends to create between

size, but in the stark outline of its peaks and rocky terraces, that may lie a mile or more beneath the Atlantic waves. No winds have smoothed and rounded its slopes since they were first formed, no rivers carry fragments year by year from the heights to fill and soften the bottom valleys. It is a silent world, unbroken even by the descent of myriads of foraminifera falling softly like snow from the surface waters above.

With the exception of a handful of its highest peaks, which thrust themselves above the waves in the Azores, in the Peak of Teneriffe, in Ascension Island, in Tristan da Cunha, the contours of the Mid-Atlantic Ridge can be traced only by the listening ear of the echo-sounder. The first rough outlines of the ridge were mapped as early as 1925, by the echo-sounders of the German research vessel *Meteor;* but it was not until 1953 that the full majesty and importance of the Mid-Atlantic Mountains were recognized, following the analysis of numerous traverses of the ridge by *Vema,* the oceanographic research vessel of Lamont Geological Observatory, New York.

This analysis, when displayed as a detailed physiographic map of the floor of the Atlantic, revealed a deep rift valley splitting the crest of the Mid-Atlantic Ridge throughout its long length from Greenland in the north to Tristan da Cunha in the south.

It was immediately recognized at Lamont that the newly discovered rift in the Mid-Atlantic Ridge coincided exactly with the belt of shallow earthquakes which was already known to extend from north to south beneath the floor of the Atlantic Ocean. That was in 1953. But by the mid-fifties seismographs had traced a 40,000-mile belt of mid-ocean earthquake epi-centres along the bottom of the Arctic Ocean, of the North and South Atlantic, of the Indian Ocean off the east coast of Africa, as well as in the South Pacific. This led Maurice Ewing and Bruce Heezen in 1956 to predict that the rifted ridge of

---

the bottom of the piston and the surface of the sediments, and hence drives the cylinder even deeper, until a core of up to 70 feet in length is forced in-side it – to be recovered by winding the whole apparatus back above the waves by means of the stout engine-driven winch on deck. (After Kullenberg and Hans Pettersen.)

Fig. 35. A section of the Mid-Atlantic ridge, showing the median rift valley which splits it along its entire length.

the Mid-Atlantic was only one section of a world-wide rift in the ocean bottom, contiguous with the earthquake belt.

During the IGY, research vessels engaged in the oceanographic programme observed isolated profiles of the mid-ocean rift valley in many parts of the world; and in early 1960 the

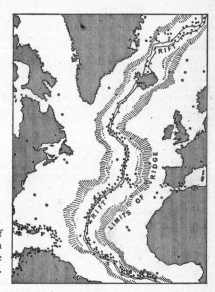

Fig. 36. The chain of shallow earthquakes which marks the path of the Mid-Atlantic rift valley. (After Heezen.)

Lamont oceanographic vessel *Vema* made a cruise in the Indian Ocean specifically to look for it – and found it, stretching all the way from Marion Island in the south to Rodriguez Island off Mauritius in the north. And, in the spring of 1962, the British hydrographic vessel H.M.S. *Owen*, with Loncarevic and Matthews of the Cambridge Geophysical Laboratory on board, brought home the news that the Indian Ocean rift valley extends still further north, right down the middle of the Carlsberg Ridge in the Arabian Sea, first discovered by the echo-sounder of the Danish vessel *Dana* in 1920–22.

Clearly we are faced here with a major feature of the topography of the earth's crust, quite as important to our understanding of crustal evolution as the mountain systems we surveyed in the last chapter. The rift valley which splits the great mid-ocean ridge throughout its length is no mere scratch in the

Fig. 37. The world-wide zone of tension in the earth's crust, scribed on the ocean floor by the rift valley atop the mid-ocean ridges. West of the East Pacific Rise, the three slender arrows at right angles to its western flank mark the strings of islands so characteristic of the Pacific – the Tuamoto Gambier, the Society, the Tuabuai Islands. The single arrow in mid-ocean traces the line of the Hawaiian Islands.

ocean floor: the profiles mapped by the echo-sounder show a steep-sided valley thousands of miles long, 6,000 feet deep, 30 miles wide; as compared with 60 miles, 4,000 feet, 10 miles for the Grand Canyon. Moreover, its physical characteristics are unique: the ocean floor below the mid-ocean ridges is hot; gravity measurements indicate a thinning of the crust in their neighbourhood; seismic observations yield a characteristic velocity below the rift valley of 7·8 km/sec, characteristic of the mantle rather than the basalt floor of the oceans. Finally, there is evidence that the whole mid-ocean ridge system is geologically young – basaltic rock dredged from the Mid-Atlantic Ridge, dated by the potassium-argon method, is a mere 10 million years old.

Now the mid-ocean rift valley comes ashore in at least two places – in the graben of Iceland and in the Great Rift Valley of East Africa which you can see in Plate 15. Both these terrestrial features have long been recognized as splits in the earth's crust, torn asunder *under tension;* and the conclusion is forced upon us that the whole mid-ocean ridge system is a *zone of tension* in the earth's crust, of comparable importance on a world scale with the mountain arc *zone of compression* dealt with in the preceding chapter.

ISLANDS IN THE PACIFIC

The topography of the Pacific Ocean is in many ways in a class apart. Already in Chapter 2 the island arc formations shoreward of the 'andesite line' have been discussed. Seaward of the andesite line lie the isolated volcanic islands, the coral atolls, and the submerged flat-topped sea-mounts which are our business in this chapter.

Tom Gaskell of the British Petroleum Company writes in his book *Under the Deep Oceans* (Eyre and Spottiswoode, 1960):

If only the sea could be drained away, the view from the great peak of Mauna Loa in Hawaii would out-rival any Japanese print of beautiful symmetrical volcanic peaks. Rising with graceful curves from a vast flat ocean-floor, the smooth slopes of the mountains would be unspoilt by the eroding action of glaciers and rivers. Some of the peaks would be like crowns, their tops encircled by a regular rim of coral rock, and most of these would be at exactly the same height, for they are the atolls which rise only a few feet above sea-level. There would be many other flat-topped peaks of lesser height, looking as if some fickle giant had arbitrarily lopped off the peaks of volcanoes to provide seats and tables. Interspersed with these would be regular cones of all sizes and ages, some smoking as a sign that nature's builders are still at work. For many years these lovely volcanic features of the Pacific have aroused speculation, especially the truncated cones which are unfamiliar on land, but the combination of seismic and echo-sounder measurements has succeeded in unravelling this mystery, so that now a single mechanism can explain them all.

In the formation of a typical volcanic island of the Pacific we may well be witnessing a repetition of the birth of the basaltic continental nuclei from the substance of the primeval crust. At first, lava from the mantle wells up through cracks in the five-mile thick ocean floor like oil from a gusher, a freely flowing viscous liquid which is quickly cooled by the surrounding water to form great heaps of porous clinker on the ocean floor. Once above the waves, however, the character of the melt alters: it solidifies in the air to form a hermetically sealed solid cap, entrapping pools of molten lava whose volume can be as much as several cubic kilometres. Then you have a volcanic island, whose cratered mountain peaks erupt violently between quiescent periods.

Now coral atolls and submerged sea-mounts alike were once just such volcanic peaks rising out of the waters of the Pacific. Then, either because the whole ocean basin began to sink, or perhaps because the ocean floor at the base of individual islands spread laterally under their weight, these volcanic peaks began to subside beneath the waves. Those rimmed by upward-growing coral reefs remain to this day with the heads above water as atolls: the vast majority – around nineteen out of twenty – sank below sea-level to become flat-topped seamounts.

Coral reefs are built by the coral polyp – a fleshy, delicate little animal form, whose portrait you see in Plate 16 – and a humble seaweed called *Zooxanthella corallinacea*, working together in symbiotic partnership.

The coral polyp itself is very sensitive to its environment: it can function only in clear sea water whose temperature lies between 68° and 90°F, with a salinity of between 27 and 40 parts per thousand. It is little else in form than a tiny flexible bottle with a hungry mouth of predatory tentacles, ready to snatch any bits and pieces of zooplankton which come drifting past on the ocean swell: so fragile that it can live only if protected by the delicate calcareous skeleton that we know familiarly as 'coral'.

Our earthbound astronomical observatories cannot take pictures of our own spiral nebula, the Milky Way, because the solar system is part of it. Here is the next-best thing – a photograph of M81 in Ursa Major, 10 million light years distant from the Mount Palomar Observatory, where this picture was taken with a 200-inch Hale telescope. The bright stars in the photograph, three of them visible against the background of the nebula itself, are all in the Milky Way.

A PANORAMIC VIEW OF THE PRODUCTS OF THE MANTLE

Top left: On the island of Java: Mount Raung in volcanic eruption.

Left: Mountain peaks in Kashmir on the east-west arm of the world-wide crustal zone of compression (see Chapter 2).

Above: In the Fiji Islands of the Pacific. The small island and village of Quoma off the east coast of Viti Levu; in the background the island of Ovalau, its chief town Levuka, once capital of Fiji.

Right: A near-vertical cliff of basalt rock on the eastern flank of the Mid-Atlantic Ridge, sunk 1,580 fathoms beneath the waves.

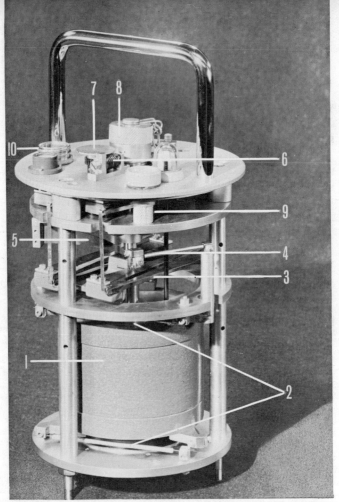

A Willmore seismometer. The heavy permanent magnet (1) is seen supported by the adjustable leaf-springs (3). The period of oscillation (0.6 to 3 seconds) is controlled, through the worm and gear-wheel (6 and 7), by altering the pressure on the spoke (4) by a leaf-spring (5). The constraining rods (2) ensure the co-axial relative movement of magnet and coil. The magnet is held in transit by the clamping-screw (8). The instrument is fully tropicalized: the coil is 'potted' in epoxy resin, the modulus of elasticity of the leaf-springs (3) is constant over the temperature range ($-40°C$ to $+50°C$), a silica-gel desiccator (9) limits the humidity within the water-tight casing.

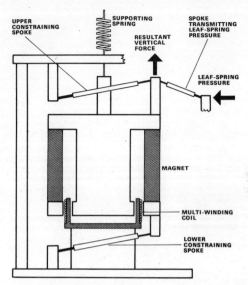

UPPER CONSTRAINING SPOKE

SUPPORTING SPRING

RESULTANT VERTICAL FORCE

SPOKE TRANSMITTING LEAF-SPRING PRESSURE

LEAF-SPRING PRESSURE

MAGNET

MULTI-WINDING COIL

LOWER CONSTRAINING SPOKE

Diagram of the mechanism for adjusting the period of oscillation of the magnet of the seismometer. Also shown is the multi-wound coil, fixed permanently between the poles of the magnet, in which an oscillating electric current is induced by the quaking magnet. This current is led via a six-pin waterproof connector – (10) on the page opposite – to a transistor amplifier, and thence to the pen which traces out the seismogram.

A seismogram of the arrival of the direct seismic wave at Pg, which has travelled through the surface rocks of the earth's crust, ahead of that at Pn of the wave which has been refracted at the Moho. A record made by a Willmore seismometer at Newton Stewart (Wigtownshire, Scotland) of the explosion of 50 kilograms of explosives detonated 180 feet deep in Loch Striven, 113 kilometers to the west.

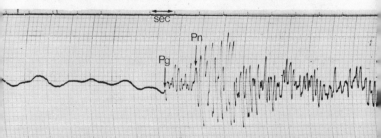

sec

Pn

Pg

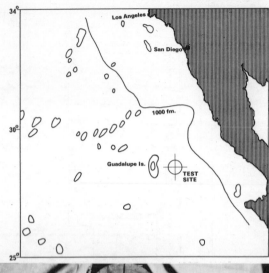

BORING A HOLE IN THE
BOTTOM OF THE SEA OFF
THE ISLAND OF GUADALUPE
Top left: The island of Guada-
lupe (after W. Bascom).
Left: Conical guide for the
drill pipe.
Above: CUSS I.
Right: Raising a length of
drill pipe.

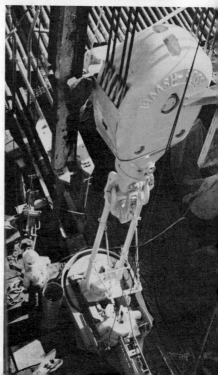

LANDSCAPES ILLUSTRATING THREE PHASES OF CONTINENTAL
GROWTH
Above left: Pillow lavas in the Keewatin province of Canada, south
of Hudson Bay, formed 2,800 million years ago.
Above right: The North Cape of Norway, on the edge of the Finno–
Scandinavian shield, aged 2,000 million years.
Below: Darjeeling, in the 1,000-million-year-old hill country of Assam.

FOUR HISTORIC OCEAN-GOING RESEARCH VESSELS
Above left: H.M.S. *Challenger* at St Paul's Rocks, in Lat. 0° 55′ N, Long. 29° 22′ W, on 28 August 1873.
Above right: Atlantis, designed by Owen and Minot of Boston, built by Burmeister and Wain at Copenhagen in 1931, for over thirty years flagship of the fleet at Woods Hole Oceanographic Institution.
Below: Meteor, the research vessel of the German Hydrographic Institute which pioneered the mapping of the topography of the ocean bottom in 1925–7.
Bottom: Discovery II, the all-purpose ocean-going laboratory of the British National Institute of Oceanography from her launch at Port Glasgow in November 1929 to her sale to ship-breakers in May 1963. Succeeded by *Discovery III*, a leading participant in the International Indian Ocean Expedition.

A modern echo-sounder (and its 'fish') recording a profile of the ocean bottom for its designer, Dr A. S. Laughton of the British National Institute of Oceanography. The recording stylus of the earlier echo-sounders has been replaced by a single-turn helical steel blade rotating against a knife edge, which sets up a point contact travelling from left to right across a moving roll of specially sensitized paper. The built-in transmitter and receiver are now housed as a single unit in the 'fish', which is towed alongside the research vessel. The old trouble of bubble formation in heavy seas between hull and water is thereby eliminated.

A bathymetric chart of the North Atlantic, made by Maurice Hill, voyaging in *Discovery II* in the summer of 1955. The overlay of strong black lines records the traverses made by the vessel while taking the echo-soundings which formed the basis of the chart.

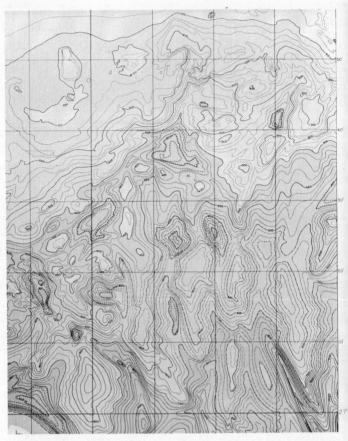

Rolling hill country at the bottom of the Gulf of Mexico off the coast of Louisiana west of New Orleans; contoured by Betty Gealy of Woods Hole Oceanographic Institution.

A turbidity current in action, as seen through the eye of the underwater camera.

The underwater camera takes a look at the abyssal plain, 4,670 metres below the surface of the east Atlantic. The 4-inch-wide track in the globigerina ooze to the left of the picture is most probably that of a holothurian or 'sea cucumber'.

The mid-ocean rift valley comes ashore – as a 'graben' in Iceland, in Kenya as the Rift Valley.

The coral polyp (*above*) and its handywork (*below*) in the atolls of the Fiji group. In the foreground of the picture below is an atoll on its way out; only the reef remains, with the wrecks of two good ships lying on its coral strand. Beyond is the coral atoll of Vatoa, all but flush with the water of its reef-encircled lagoon.

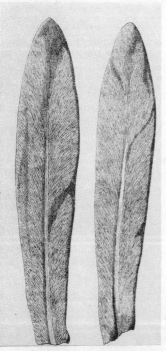

Above: Two species of Equisetales, or 'horse-tails', fossils found in the Allegheny carboniferous deposits in the United States; their botanical names are *Asterophyllites equisetiformis* and (appropriately enough) *Annularia asteris*. The top right-hand corner shows the terminal leaves of a branch of *A. equisetiformis* still unfolded.

Left: Two leaves of *Glossopteris decipiens* from the State of Bihar in India. The contrast between these tongue-shaped leaves of the temperate-zone carboniferous forests and the horse-tail form of the tropical giants is so marked as to need no further explanation.

Two ends of the same Laurasian transcurrent fault – the Cabot Fault in Nova Scotia and the Great Glen in the Scottish Highlands.
Above: The Sunrise Valley on the Cabot Trail, sheltered by the tree-covered slopes of the North Mountain. *Below:* Loch Oich, with Loch Ness in the southern distance and Invergarry Castle in the foreground.

The San Andreas Fault, looking north from the air above Indio, California.

Above: Trade-wind clouds voyaging south to the Equator.
Below: Cloud-tower water-vapour pump in full action, caught by an airborne camera off Puerto Rico at a height of 5,000 feet.

Cyclone photographed by Tiros IV, 18 May 1962, in Long. 8° E, Lat. 50° S approximately.

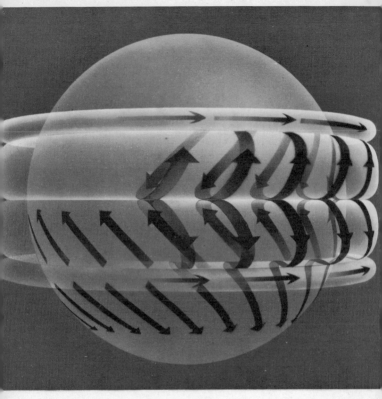

The trade-wind cell. The surface easterlies of the sub-tropics converge at the Equator and are swept aloft. Edging north and south
in turbulent eddies, 20,000 feet up, the once moisture-laden air, now
dry and cold, meets the sub-tropical jet-streams – geostrophic winds
circling the earth in latitudes 30° N and 30° S – up under the roof of
the troposphere. Compressed against the barrier of the jet-streams,
the cold dry air sinks to earth, where it diverges north and south,
south and north – to give us our surface westerlies north and south
of 30° N and 30° S, and a rebirth of the surface trades blowing towards the Equator.

How the off-shore winds of the winter monsoon give rise to the up-welling of bottom water. The consequent increase in the photo-synthesized phytoplankton of the surface water is dramatic. The life chain of the sea uncoils link by link. Soon the big edible fish converge on the nutrient area. Empty bellies ashore are filled.

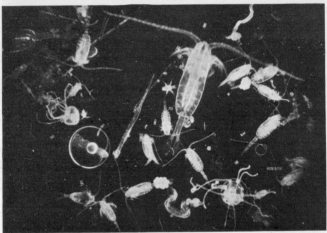

Above: Phytoplankton, the grass of the sea meadows. At least three different families can be seen: several species of *Chaetoceros* (diatoms in chains armed with spines); *Thalassiosira condensata* (the shining white chain at bottom left); and *Lauderia borealis* to the right of the latter. (×90)

Below: Zooplankton, first link in the chain of animal life in the sea. Two species of copepod (one represented by the largest animal, the other by several specimens of a smaller variety, two with a cluster of eggs); two little medusas, with their circular domes and long tentacles; a circular fish egg at left centre, with a young arrow-worm to its right; a larval copepod between the arrow-worm and the large copepod; two tunicate worms (top right and bottom centre). (×11)

The external skeleton of the coral polyp is however too fragile to build a coral reef: and it is here that *Zooxanthella* takes over. This tiny one-celled alga feeds on the waste products of the polyp, and in exchange supplies the coral with an ample amount of carbonate with which to build a stout sea-wall against the ocean breakers.

Thus where a sinking volcanic cone was surrounded at contemporary sea-level with a coral reef, coral polyp and its companion alga could build upward fast enough to beat the rate of subsidence (about two centimetres per thousand years) of their island. The sinking top of the peak would at one stage get lopped off by the ocean breakers, which would also scour out the familiar lagoon inland from the protecting reef.

This picture of the formation of coral atolls, first advocated by Charles Darwin during the classic voyage of the *Beagle* in 1835, was for years the subject of heated debate; but a combination of modern seismic prospecting and deep drilling have in the last decade established beyond dispute that the coral crown of a Pacific atoll does indeed rest below sea level on basaltic volcanic rock.

The flat-topped sea-mounts which stud the floor of the Pacific are now seen to be either atolls that didn't make the grade, or else sunken volcanic peaks once upthrust in waters which were unsuitable for the coral polyp. Their flat tops mark the stage in their subsidence when they were just awash: when the pounding of the Pacific surf would shear off their friable laval tops to give the truncated cones which the modern echo-sounder records in their hundreds. Too, there would appear to be as many hundreds which have eventually merged with the ocean floor, leaving no trace of their once proud peaks behind: for surrounding the base of each sunken cone is a so-called 'apron', the shape of which strongly supports the suggestion on page 92 of slow lateral creep outwards from the periphery.

Assuming the rate of subsidence of 2 cm/1,000 yrs quoted above, one can calculate that any island more than 250 million years old (i.e., pre-Cretaceous) should by now have totally disappeared, presumably spreading the sediments accumulated through the years on its summit and flanks over the surrounding ocean floor. Yet here comes a very remarkable fact: that no lavas, no fossils either in the islands or on the surrounding sea-bed, no sediments in the Pacific, are older than the 250-million-year-old Cretaceous period. Now this same period saw the latest stage of mountain building, in the formation of the island arcs of the China seas; it saw the completion of the switch in the earth's zone of compressive fracture of the western margin of North America, from the Appalachians in the east to the Andes in the south; and in all probability it saw the growth of the Mid-Atlantic Ridge.

Thus the comparatively recent intense volcanic activity in the Pacific basin, when viewed in a world-wide perspective, is seen as only one aspect of great changes in the surface features of the earth, during which the continents took their present stations on the globe and the oceans their present pattern. In the next chapter we shall discover how these changes came about.

CHAPTER FOUR

Drifting Continents

THE discovery during the last decade of a world-wide complex of
mid-ocean ridges, when set beside the earlier recognition of a
great T-shaped belt of linked mountain arcs bordering the
continents, has given us a completely new picture of the earth's
crust: a picture not of one, but of two mountain systems of
global extent. Significantly, both systems are seismically active:
the island arcs and trenches being characterized by deep-focus
earthquakes, the rift valley of the great mid-ocean ridge by shallow earthquakes; both are hinged to earth's mantle. But whereas
the active mountains arcs on land delineate a zone of crustal fracture under *compression*, the mid-ocean ridges are torn apart along
their centre by a rift valley under *tension*. At the bottom of the
deep trenches which border on the mountain arcs, the crust is
sucked down into the mantle; whereas the substance of the
mantle wells upwards into the bed of the mid-ocean rift
valleys.

CONVECTION CURRENTS IN THE MANTLE

These are facts: and facts demand an explanation. There have
indeed been quite a few hypotheses aiming to interpret the facts
of ocean trench and ridge in the accepted language of solid-earth
geophysics; but only one such has over the period 1950–65
shown signs of arriving at the status of a self-consistent theory:
namely that originally advocated by the late Vening Meinesz of
Utrecht postulating the existence of *convection currents* in the
mantle. The injection of the crust into the substance of the
upper mantle beneath the trenches, the extrusion of magma from
the mantle into the mid-ocean rift valley, would then be plausibly
explained as the outward and visible sign of convection cells in
the body of the mantle itself.

Now it has already been made clear that the elastic properties
of the earth's interior appropriate to the analysis of seismic waves

are those of matter effectively under instantaneous stress; and that in the opposite case of a hot body subject to small stresses over a long period of time, slow creep of the material of the body proceeds along the lines of strain. Nevertheless, it is perhaps worth while to pin down this matter of the time-scale of the assumed convective processes in the mantle once again and once and for all.

Thus taking the diameter of a convection cell, supposed for the moment to be in one plane, as say 3,000 kilometres, and the rate of convective creep at the circumference of the cell as 1 cm per year, then the time required for one complete internal turn-over is 300 million years. In short, we have to do here with a geological time-scale, such as that of the geological column of Fig. 18.

CONVECTION CURRENTS AND SURFACE TOPOGRAPHY

Certain questions arise: Can we frame a *pattern* of convection cells in the mantle which fits the present crustal topography of the globe? Can we determine the *number* of convection cells which would be reflected in the upwelling of the substance of the mantle under the rift valley of the ocean-bottom mountain chain; and conversely, its downward motion below the trenches that lie off the margins of the continents?

A tentative answer to these questions has been supplied by the same man who back in the twenties first mooted the then radically bold suggestion that convection currents in the mantle might account for the negative gravity anomalies which he had observed from his submarine as it traversed the deep ocean trenches of the Pacific. For in the year 1951 Vening Meinesz organized in his native Holland the analysis of over 40,000 contour diagrams of the elevation of the earth's surface at as many places on the globe, in terms of a hypothetical pattern of 30 convection cells, the predominance of a certain number of which over the remainder in the total convection pattern should find its reflection in the observed surface topography. The number which fulfils this condition turns out to be *five* (Fig. 38).

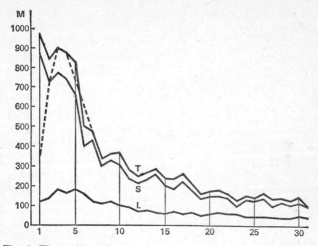

Fig. 38. The earth's surface topography, as it emerges from an analysis of gravity measurements, made at the surface, by the mathematical method of 'spherical harmonics'. In the figure, T means total topography, S ocean-floor topography, L continental topography. Note how the centre of gravity of all three cluster round the line of the fifth harmonic $n = 5$. (After Vening Meinesz.)

CONVECTION PATTERNS IN THE PAST

Hark back for the moment to the picture of the present phase in the evolution of the interior of the earth illustrated in Fig. 2; and recall that the words 'present phase' were used advisedly in the accompanying text. For if the process of cold accretion postulated for the evolution of the planets is correct, then it follows that the earth's liquid nickel-iron core has grown at the expense of the surrounding mantle during the past 3,000 million years. How then has the pattern of convection currents adapted itself over this period of time to the changing thickness of the mantle?

An answer to this question has been given by Runcorn of Newcastle-upon-Tyne, as the result of an elegant theoretical analysis, which calls for four successive steps in an increasing number of convection cells, beginning in the morning of the earth's history with a single cell, and ending as of today with five – the same number as Vening Meinesz arrives at from his particular angle of approach.

This number of course tags the same spherical harmonic $n = 5$ as bobs up in Fig. 38; but even if we admit the droll comment of E. N. Lyustikh of Moscow on 'the blind use of spherical harmonics' in the analysis of geophysical problems, we have to

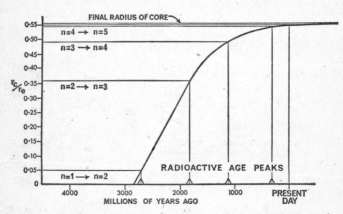

Fig. 39. The pattern of convection cells in the substance of the mantle changes kaleidoscopically as the ratio $r_c : r_e$ of the radii of core and earth assumes a succession of four discrete values. Each such critical change can be identified, within the spread of the still meagre number of measurements, with the four successive bursts of mountain building signalled by the age-peaks in the radio-active dating of the rocks. (After Runcorn.)

agree that Runcorn's phenomenological angle of approach is a long way off that of Vening Meinesz.

Runcorn, however, goes further: he seeks to identify the successive stages of increase in the number of convection cells demanded by his theory with the successive bursts of world-wide mountain building which the radio-active clocks signal as having occurred 2,600, 1,800, 1,000, and 250 million years ago.

How he does this is illustrated in Fig. 39, where the ratio $r_c : r_e$ of the radii of liquid core and of the earth itself is plotted against time. If now with Runcorn we make the final assumption

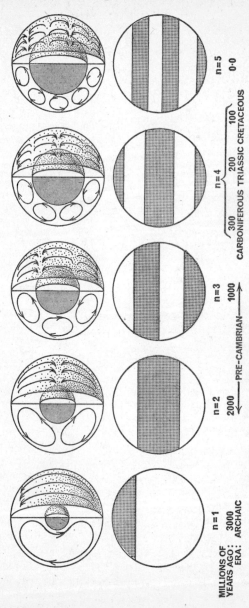

MILLIONS OF YEARS AGO: 3000   2000   1000   300   200   100   0·0

ERA: ARCHAIC   PRE-CAMBRIAN   CARBONIFEROUS TRIASSIC CRETACEOUS

n=1   n=2   n=3   n=4   n=5

Fig. 40. The inner core of the earth grows at the expense of the mantle as the iron content of the mantle is surrendered to it. (After Runcorn.)

that the *rate* at which iron from the mantle is surrendered to the liquid core is proportional to the surface area of the core and to the mass of iron remaining in the mantle, then the growth of the core follows the curve shown in the figure, trending parallel to the time axis as the present epoch is approached.

CRUSTAL TOPOGRAPHY IN THE PAST

The effect of these changes in the economy of the earth's interior on the external topography of the globe is illustrated schematically in Fig. 40, on the argument that the continental rafts – or more accurately 'icebergs' – which float upon the upper mantle, find their positions of equilibrium where two descending convection currents meet.

A careful reading of this illustration, in parallel with the geological column of Fig. 18, yields the following interpretation:

1. 2,000 million years ago, in the Pre-Cambrian era, there was but one land mass on the earth's surface, of which presumably the ancient continental shields are now the only remnant ($n = 1$).

2. 1,000 million years ago, two large land masses, corresponding to the Laurasia and Gondwanaland of Alfred Wegener and Alexander du Toit, are found: Laurasia lying athwart the Equator, Gondwanaland covering a region centred on the South Pole ($n = 3$).

3. 300 million years ago, in the Carboniferous period, Laurasia and Gondwanaland are still present; a third land mass now appears, centred on the North Pole ($n = 4$).

4. Between 250 and 100 million years ago, that is from mid-Permian to mid-Cretaceous, the crustal kaleidoscope changes its pattern once again, this time to that of the present day: Gondwanaland breaks up, Laurasia splits in two, the land around the North Pole is flooded out ($n = 5$).

Thus the hypothesis of convection currents in the mantle leads straight to the assertion – or perhaps better re-assertion – of the doctrine of continental drift, for so long the subject of frequently acrimonious debate with the geologists, wedded as they were – and often still are – to the 'Principle of Uniformity' pronounced in 1785 by Hutton.

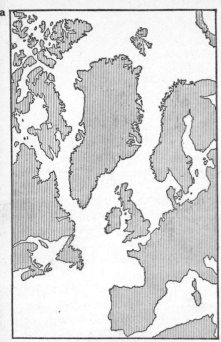

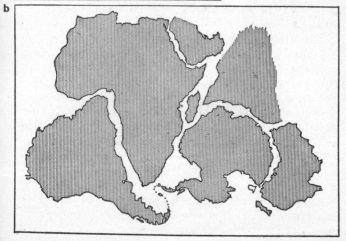

Fig. 41. The proto-continents Laurasia and Gondwanaland.

CONTINENTAL DRIFT

Now so long as the evidence for continental drift lay within the province of geology alone, so long that is as the criteria were those cited by the pioneers Wegener and du Toit – physiographical, stratigraphical, paleontological – the situation from an olympian viewpoint was largely a matter of looking on either one or the other face of the same coin: the 'drifters' demanded shifting continents and a reasonably consistent climatic zoning over the globe during geological time; while the 'anti-drifters' shouted for fixed continents and a global climate that they could select at will to match the evidence of fossil animals and plants belonging to any one geological epoch.

Since around the year 1950, however, a fresh complexion has been put on the whole subject, thanks to the emergence of two virtually new subjects of study – the study of the ocean floor on the one hand, and the study of the magnetism of the rocks on the other.

The floor of the oceans has, as we have seen, its own unique character, radically different from that of the continents: primitive basalt as against granitic rocks – whether pristine, metamorphosed, or sedimentized. The basalt of the ocean floor is invariably young – a mere 250 million years at most. There are few sediments on the ocean floor older than Cretaceous, which accounts for the thin layer they present to the echo-sounder. And finally, there is ample evidence that the material of the ocean floors is creeping horizontally away from either side of the mid-ocean ridges towards the adjacent continents.

The continental rocks, for their part, have been found to contain a new kind of fossil – fossil magnetism – which can be used to log the course of a drifting continent from its port of departure in the distant past to its present port of call.

PALEOMAGNETISM

Basic to the method of paleomagnetism in locating the past positions of selected sites in the earth's crust is the assumption that the earth's magnetic field, when averaged over several thousands of years, is a geocentric dipole field directed along the axis of rotation. This looks a bit odd at first sight, because we all know that the geocentric dipole is currently inclined at an angle of $11\frac{1}{2}°$ to the axis of rotation, so that the north magnetic pole lies in Northern Canada; and that tables of magnetic declination are issued annually to navigators who wish to use a magnetic compass. Nevertheless, a refinement of the dynamo theory of the earth's magnetic field, already dealt with in Chapter 1, shows that the axial dipole field predicted by the theory is indeed a geocentric axially symmetric field, over a time scale given by the stream-line velocity in the liquid core divided by the length scale of the eddy currents; a quantity in dimensional agreement with the basic premiss of paleomagnetism.

This granted, we may look again at the fossil magnets. These are grains of iron- or nickel-bearing substances which are frequently found frozen into the substance of once-molten lavas, or held fast in the material of sedimentary rocks which were once mobile mud or shifting sand. At the time when either lava or sandstone was laid down, we must suppose that these magnetic granules aligned themselves, and were permanently magnetized, in the direction of the earth's magnetic field appropriate to that time and place. Cemented into position when lava or sediment solidified, they are the fossilized trace of the earth's magnetic field prevailing at their original place of deposition in bygone geological areas – always provided that the rocks have not subsequently been reworked by either volcanic or igneous action.

Turn now to Fig. 42, and notice how a freely suspended magnetic needle, aligned in the direction of the earth's magnetic lines of force at its point of suspension, lies horizontally at the Equator, but dips – north-seeking pole downwards in the northern hemisphere, south-seeking pole downwards in the southern hemisphere – always more steeply as it approaches either pole. By measuring the angle of magnetic dip, in fact, a man can determine his *geographical latitude* without recourse to the stars.

Hence by measurements made on the angle of magnetic dip of rock specimens from a particular place on the earth, we deduce their *ancient latitude*. And by a similar determination of their magnetic declination, we can determine the ancient *horizontal orientation* of those same rocks. As Patrick Blackett of Imperial College in London, a pioneer of paleomagnetism applied to continental drift, so succinctly puts it: 'The paleomagnetist is in exactly the same position as a seaman only able to observe the altitude of the pole star. He can deduce the

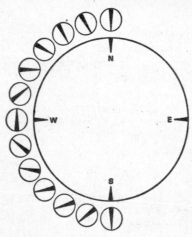

Fig. 42. The dip-needle is a tell-tale of today's latitude; magnetic fossils are the dip needles of the past.

orientation of his ship and its latitude but can say nothing about its longitude.'

Thus paleomagnetism has nothing to say *directly* on for example the question of whether North America and Europe were once nearer or father apart than they are today; although indirectly very valuable conclusions can be drawn from the magnetic orientation *in situ* of rock specimens drawn from different continents, as we shall see.

THE PRE-MESOZOIC HISTORY OF GONDWANALAND

Between 400 million and 250 million years ago, Gondwanaland was drifting slowly across the Antarctic circle from east to west. Throughout this ancient voyage, the enormous proto-continent drifted as one single unit. The break-up into the continents of South America, Africa, India, Australia, Antarctica was still to come.

There are two bodies of evidence which support this statement; the evidence of paleomagnetism, and the evidence of the ancient climates of Gondwanaland; and these will now be considered in turn.

The paleomagnetic evidence we present comes from two independent witnesses – K. M. Creer of Newcastle-upon-Tyne, and P. M. S. Blackett of Imperial College, London. Creer's evidence concerns South America, Blackett's Australia: that is, the leading edge and trailing edge respectively of the voyaging protocontinent of Fig. 41(b). The ancient latitudes of South America and Australia, taking Brazilia and Alice Springs

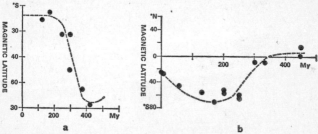

a   b

Fig. 43. The Paleomagnetic log of the voyages of South America and Australia within the past 500 million years. (After Creer and Blackett respectively.)

respectively as continental reference points, are plotted against time in Figs. 43(a and b); and pictorially, with the ancient orientations included, in Figs. 44 (a and b).

There are several interesting points to notice in these figures. For example, in Creer's pictures of South America, we observe that in the late Permian, Tierra del Fuego was actually nearer the South Pole than Rio de Janeiro; while from Figs. 43(b) and 44(b) we can read that Australia was moving polewards up to and including the Triassic. But the most significant comparison that can be made in the present context is that between the then contemporary ancient latitudes of Brazilia and Alice Springs. Thus 300 million years ago for example, the ancient latitude of

Brazilia was 75°S; Alice Springs was situated just south of the Equator; when Australia was logged at 80°S, South America was in latitude 35°S. Thus there can be no question of a uniform ancient climate common to the huge expanse of all Gondwanaland; on the contrary, we have even to expect antipathetic

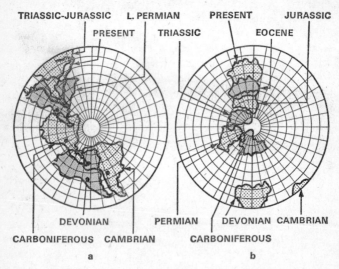

Fig. 44. The voyage of South America and Australia, as segments of continental Gondwanaland, across the Antarctic Circle. (After Creer and Runcorn respectively.)

changes of climate at its extreme eastern and western borders – and that is precisely what the paleoclimatologists find to be the case.

Now the modern paleoclimatologist, unlike his forbears, doesn't favour the idea of successive total changes of world climate in the past; he lays down as his most important single tenet that climatic zoning as we know it today is valid for geological time, at least from the first known appearance of life 750 million years ago in the Proterozoic onwards. True, the tropical zone may have been narrower or wider in the Tertiary period than it is today, as was the arctic zone in the northern hemisphere during the glacial epoch of the Quaternary; but by and large the atmospheric heat engine functioned in the past much as it does now.

So it becomes possible to lay down certain self-consistent *climatic indicators*, which shall point to the ancient climate enjoyed by a given continental area in any era represented in the geological column. This has been done for Gondwanaland by Blackett as in the following table:

TABLE 2

Climatic Indicators	Climatic Zone
Extensive glaciation; coal deposits; *Glossopteris*	Polar and half temperate
Large insects, and reptiles; minor glaciations	Temperate and half arid
Salt, gypsum, and corals	Equatorial and half arid

Now if you were to aim at increasing the bulk of an otherwise slender volume by filling up a lot of pages with print, you could proceed to a lengthy verbal description of the paleoclimates of old Gondwanaland. We prefer another table, from which all the necessary information can be extracted at a glance.

Even a casual look at Table 3 is sufficient to bring out the important fact that Antarctica and Australia are laggards in traversing the successive climatic zones which eventually all segments of Gondwanaland alike experienced in their turn; and contrariwise, South America steps somewhat ahead of the others. This is completely in accord with the itinerary followed by Gondwanaland in its east-west journey across the Antarctic circle, according to the paleomagnetic record of its rocks.

A word about the Gondwanaland coal measures, of which the typical plant indicator is *Glossopteris*. This well-grown plant with its characteristic tongue-shaped leaf is very different from the giant horse-tails of the coalbeds typical of the northern hemisphere. *Equisitae* are plants adapted to a swampy subsoil and a humid atmosphere – preferably a tropical swamp, soaked with a tropical rainfall: hence the text-book picture of *all* coal

TABLE 3

Relevant Geological Periods in Gondwanaland Segments

Climatic Indicator	Climatic Zone	South America	Africa	India	Antarctica	Australia
Salt, gypsum and corals	Equatorial and half arid	Jurassic	Jurassic / Triassic / Late Permian	Jurassic / Triassic / Late Permian	[Devonian] / Jurassic	[Devonian] / Jurassic
Large insects, also reptiles (Mesosaurus); minor glaciations	Temperate and half arid	Triassic / Late Permian / Early Permian (Brazil)	Late Permian / Early Permian	Early Permian	Permian	Triassic
Glaciations coupled with Glossopteris; Coal measures	Polar and half temperate	Late Carboniferous (Brazil) / Early Carboniferous (Argentine)	Carboniferous	Permo-Carboniferous	Permo-Carboniferous	Permian

measures of the Carboniferous as the remains of a steaming forest of fleshy trees. The coal measures of Gondwanaland stem from a much more highly developed plant, which asked for a *temperate* climate (see Plate 17) and which was very possibly the ancestor of the flowering plants of the northern hemisphere, the fossilized skeletons of which appear in such sudden profusion in post-Cretaceous strata in such separated lands as northern Latin America, Africa, India and Australia.

Now the invariable association of *Glossopteris* with the glacial tillites of Gondwanaland means that here was no ice-age such as North America and Europe suffered in the Quaternary. Glaciers, true; but not necessarily extensive ice-sheets. The climate in which glaciers flowed down from the higher lands, in which the *Glossopteris* coal measures were laid down, was a temperate climate comparable to say Switzerland or Norway today.

The glacial tillites of Gondwanaland, incidentally, are wonderfully clear finger-posts to the correctness of the reconstruction of Fig. 41(b). Look at Fig. 45 and see how the pebble-scribed

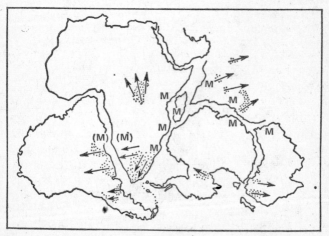

Fig. 45. The glacial tillites (stippled areas) of ancient Gondwanaland are striated in the directions of the arrows, thus betraying the *glacial flow-lines*. The sites at which the simultaneous appearance of Jurassic *marine deposits* has been established are marked M in the figure; (M) denotes the later (early Cretaceous) marine deposits on the coastlines of Brazil and Angola.

striations of the ancient tillites are always directed away from the South Pole.

A third point – in a sense non-scientific – should not fail to be made here: namely, that even in the late fifties, Antarctica was geologically *terra incognita;* so that the best-informed paleoclimatologists were forced to leave blanks in their monographs when the ancient climate of Antarctica came up for discussion. Five years into the sixties, and Antarctica fairly hums with the dialogue of scientific exploration between Americans and Russians, French and English, New Zealanders and Scots: and entries can be made for Antarctica in our Table that are almost on a par with the remainder (see insert, Fig. 46).

All this has been made possible by the signature in Washington D.C. on 9 December 1959, in the name of no fewer than twelve nations, of the Antarctic Treaty, and by its formal ratification on 23 June 1961, a treaty which froze all territorial claims in Antarctica for thirty years. The Preamble to the Treaty speaks for itself –

Recognising that it is in the interest of all mankind that Antarctica shall continue forever to be used exclusively for peaceful purposes and shall not become the scene or object of international discord . . .

Convinced that the establishment of a firm foundation for the continuation and development of such cooperation on the basis of freedom of scientific investigation in Antarctica as applied during the International Geophysical Year accords with the interest of science and the progress of all mankind;

Convinced also that a treaty insuring the use of Antarctica for peaceful purposes only and the continuance of international harmony in Antarctica will further the purposes and principles embodied in the charter of the United Nations; . . .

– as do the words of Laurence M. Gould, spoken before the U.S. Senate Committee on Foreign Relations with traditional American eloquence, as Chairman of the Committee on Polar Research of the National Academy of Sciences of the United States:

I believe the Antarctic Treaty is a breakthrough of historic importance. I believe the IGY and especially the Antarctic program has laid new foundations for unifying our planet. It ushered in a new world of cooperation. I believe if the spirit which obtained during the IGY and which finds expression in the Antarctic Treaty is nourished and spreads as it should, history may take a new and more hopeful direction in our time.

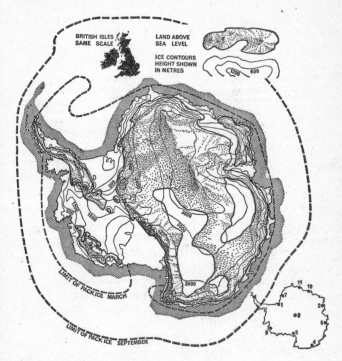

Fig. 46. Antarctica. This modern map, compiled by the U.S. Geological Survey from hundreds of seismic profiles, shows that under the ice is hidden a true continental land mass bordered on the west by an island archipelago. The archipelago is structurally an extension of South America, geologically younger than the adjoining Antarctic continent.

The inset represents 'Antarctica of the Twelve Nations', of which ten occupied the stations marked with a numbered full circle during the winter of 1965. They are: (1) Argentina (General Belgrado); (2) Australia (Mawson); (3) Chile (General Bernardo O'Higgins); (4) France (Dumont d'Urville); (5) New Zealand (Scott); (6) USSR (Mirny); (7) United Kingdom (Halley Bay); (8) USA (Amundsen-Scott South Pole); (9) USA (New Byrd); (10) Belgium/Netherlands (Roi Baudouin); (11) South Africa (Sanae.)

The Antarctic Treaty is indispensable in the world of science which knows no national or other political boundaries; but it is a document unique in history which may take its place alongside the Magna Carta and other great symbols of man's quest for enlightenment and order.

In sober truth, there is no cold war in Antarctica. In fact, the political climate is positively Jurassic!

THE BREAK-UP OF GONDWANALAND

The picture of for example South America partially circum-navigating the South Pole from east to west, as illustrated in Fig. 44(a), could have been presented as one of the pole wander-ing across the continent from west to east; and in point of fact, the paleomagneticians frequently find a presentation of *apparent polar wandering* the more convenient and succint. And indeed it could well be that the imbalance of two such gigantic super-continents as Laurasia astraddle the equator and Gondwanaland in the south caused an actual slippage of the whole of the earth's crust over the underlying upper mantle.

Be that as it may, the so-called 'polar wandering curve' has proved to be a sovereign method of discovering whether two land masses have held together or have separated in the past; for in the first case their polar wandering curves can be super-posed, in the second case they will diverge one from the other. Fig. 47, due to Creer, illustrates the application of this method to South America and Africa; and at once one can say that the two continents remained juxtaposed as segments of Gondwana-land until the pole position for Africa labelled 16, which refers to magnetic fossils dating from the Permian-Triassic, age 220 million years; a date which marks the initial separation of Africa and South America. If now Australia is taken as a marker, then the same technique reveals that the remainder of Gondwanaland began to disintegrate some 30 million years earlier than the western fragment South America: Africa.

Thus the sequence of events according to the paleomagnetic evidence is: first a fragmentation involving South America and Africa as a single unit, plus India, Antarctica and Australia in simultaneous separation; and second the separation of Africa from South America.

This reconstruction of the later history of Gondwanaland is in beautiful agreement with the *simultaneous appearance of marine deposits* in the Jurassic on the east coast of Africa,

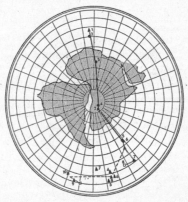

Fig. 47. Apparent polar wandering curves of South America and Africa. (Creer.)

Madagascar, on both the west and east coasts of India – as also of Australia; whereas marine deposits first appear in Angola and Brazil, again simultaneously, in the early Cretaceous period (see Fig. 45). You can almost see the gradual penetration of the oceans with their fauna along the newly formed coastlines!

A particularly vivid impression of the first fragmentation of Gondwanaland is got from the magnetic log of India, as spelled out by Blackett and his school at Imperial College. A pictorial representation of the long voyage of India, cruising speed around three centimetres a year, from its ancient anchorage alongside Antarctica to its docking against the northern shore of the Tethys Sea, is seen in Fig. 48. Startling confirmation of this arrival of India off the ancient South-Asian coast comes from the intensive investigation of the floor of the Indian Ocean during the years 1960–65 of the International Indian Ocean Expedition (p. 165). Thus Bruce Heezen reports what he calls a 'microcontinent' in

the linear aseismic ridge running due north-south between the
Maldive islands and the Chagos group, which could be regarded
as a fragment of the Indian land mass left behind in the substance of the upper mantle. Moreover, the research ship *Argo*,
from the Scripps Institution, working the Maldive-Chagos area
in October 1962, could identify the volcanic lavas from the ridge
as the origin of the celebrated 'Deccan traps' of India, which lie
on a line extending northward from the ridge: both lavas being
of the same age, namely the early Eocene.

Thus India came finally to rest against the ancient Himalayan
island arc; indeed, there is good geological evidence that its
northern edge carried its Gondwanaland strata forward to a
gigantic underthrust of the South Asian continental margin,
uplifting the Himalayas and the Tibetan plateau to become the
highest mountain region on the globe.

In a less violent fashion, the South American land mass made
a near approach to the ancient coast of North America; and the
compressional zone of fracture on the Californian coast switched
direction from eastwards towards the Appalachians to southward along the line of the Andes: which event, as we have already

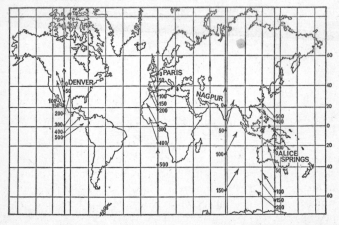

Fig. 48. The paleomagnetic record of continental drift referred to the latitudes
of the four key towns Denver, Paris, Nagpur and Alice Springs. (After
Blackett et al.)

seen in Chapter 2, other evidence places in time as mid-Mesozoic: although there would appear to be a discrepancy here between the dating of the Appalachian island arc system as Paleozoic, and that of the opening of the North Atlantic (see below) as early Permian. The relationship of the Caribbean system to North and South America in the light of these events is likewise still obscure.

LAURASIA, NORTHWARD-BOUND

The Laurasian land mass during the Upper Paleozoic and Meso-zoic eras was according to Fig. 40 (n = 4), centred on the Equator. Do the magnetic logs of North America and Europe record their journey north together to their present latitudes; and do their polar wandering curves tell us when they became separated by the North Atlantic Ocean? The answer is Yes to both these questions.

Blackett has assembled the paleomagnetic and paleoclimato-logical evidence for the northward drift of North America and Europe; his findings are summarized in Table 4.

There remains one striking line of evidence which has not been considered by Blackett: we mean the evidence of *paleo-winds* – fossil winds imprinted on the aeolian sandstones of the United States, Mexico, the British Isles.

Most of us have seen and admired the beautiful contours carved by the winds on the sand-dunes in-shore. Some of us have been lucky enough to have seen and heard the true aeolian sand-hills of the North African desert. Just such ripple-marks and downwind accumulation of the sands have been found frozen into the dune sandstones of for example Wyoming and Arizona in the United States, and into the dune fields which stretch from Morayshire in the north to Devon in the south of the British Isles – witnesses to the winds prevailing over these lands in the Permian. The latter system is illustrated in Fig. 49, from which it will be seen that the winds blow from the north-east: in other words, 250 million years ago Britain lay in the northern trade-wind belt, five thousand miles or so south of its present latitude.

TABLE 4: Ancient Climates of Europe and North America

Age in millions of years between		Climatic Zone		λm (Europe)	Range of Latitude between L_1 and L_2				λm (USA)
T_1	T_2	Europe	USA		Europe L_1	L_2	USA L_1	L_2	
0	35	Temperate and polar		46	45	90			
35	180	Arid and equatorial		33	0	45			
180	270	Arid	Arid	17	15	45	15	45	30
270	350	Equatorial	Equatorial	5	0	15	0	15	5
350	400	Equatorial and half arid	Equatorial and half arid	5	0	30	0	30	5
400	600	Arid and temperate		21	15	70			

Fig. 49. Paleo winds in ancient sand-dunes of the British Isles. (Opdyke.)

THE ATLANTIC OCEAN OPENS

One of the oldest games of the 'drifters' has been the attempted fitting of the coast lines of the lands lying on opposite sides of the Atlantic. These attempts invariably failed in detail, because, as we now know, the true margin of a continent is the continental slope, and not the visible coast-line. How perfect the fit is between the lands of the North Atlantic can be seen from Fig. 41(a), which is the assembly achieved by Bullard and co-workers in Cambridge, using the 500-fathom line as the continental border and an unprejudiced computer as judge of the best fit.

Let us take, as a specific example of what this fit means in terms of past geological formations, the demonstration by Tuzo Wilson of Toronto that the Great Glen of the Scottish highlands and the Cabot Fault of Eastern North America were once two ends of the same transcurrent fault.

. Canadian geologists have long been familiar with a narrow belt of transcurrent faults off the east coast of North America: namely the large fault which forms the eastern side of the Northern Peninsula in Newfoundland; the faults which have been

Fig. 50. The 'Cabot Fault' of the east coast of North America. (After Tuzo Wilson.)

clearly mapped in northern Cape Breton Island, in Nova Scotia, across the isthmus from Cape George to Cape Chignecto; hints that the latter fault extends beyond the Bay of Fundy to one which is known to lie off the coast of New Brunswick. It is to the credit of Tuzo Wilson that he has collated all these facts, and demonstrated that we are dealing here with segments of one great transcurrent fault, which he has named the Cabot Fault (Fig. 50).

Now Glen Mor is the Paleozoic contemporary of the Cabot Fault: its rocks are similar, its strike is similar, and the horizontal shift of the rocks on the left-hand side of the fault relative to those on the right is in the same sense and of comparable magnitude. You can convince yourself that Tuzo Wilson is on the right track when he claims the Great Glen and his Cabot Fault as a single ancient feature of Laurasia, by looking closely at the south-west trend of the Highland Fault across northern Ireland to Newfoundland in Fig. 41(a); see also Plate 18.

Now comes the evidence for the opening up of the North Atlantic; and again it is Creer who has shown that the polar wandering curves for North America and Europe (including U.S.S.R.) step together through the Upper Paleozoic, until they part company in the early Permian, some 260 million years ago. The North Atlantic then started to open up, and by the end of the Cretaceous period Europe and North America had taken their present stations on the map of the world. The opening up of the North Atlantic, be it noted, began around 50 million years before that of the South Atlantic, heralded by the separation of South America and Africa as the second stage in the disintegration of Gondwanaland. . . .

There is a rather charming sidelight to this pulling apart of South America and Africa. It concerns the natural history of the Green Turtle. A posse of this species mate and nest each year on Ascension Island. They come from an area around Rio Doce in Brazil. This involves an annual journey of 1,400 miles each way. It also entails considerable navigational expertise on the part of the nesting turtle, even with the 68°F isotherm of the surface waters to guide her. But go back 150 million years, and those Green Turtles would have only a narrow arm of the sea to negotiate; for since the ancient latitudes of Rio Doce and the projection of Ascension on the African coast are in precise agreement, the nesting ground was lying there just across the water, a mere hundred miles or so from its land based home among the elephant grass of east Brazil.

THE BIRTH OF THE MID-ATLANTIC RIDGE

The opening up of the Atlantic Ocean, north and south, saw the birth of the Mid-Atlantic Ridge, and the lateral spread of the ocean bottom east and west of the central spine. This spreading of the ocean floor can actually be followed in time by a study of the pattern of magnetic anomalies exhibited by the primitive basaltic crust. . . .

The interpretation of this pattern by Vine and Matthews of Cambridge depends on the phenomenon of magnetic reversal of the earth's dipole field. Spontaneous rhythmic reversals of the

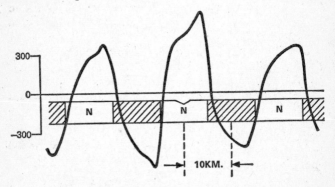

Fig. 51. Schematic diagram of the magnetic reversals in the floor of the Atlantic east and west of the Mid-Atlantic Ridge, matched against the periods of normal and reversed magnetization (γ) recognized by Cox; from which the rate of spreading of the ocean floor can be calculated to be about 1 cm/yr. (After Vine and Matthews.)

direction of its magnetic field is a well-known characteristic of the Faraday disc dynamo, which we have seen in Chapter 1 to give a reasonable explanation of the origin of the dipole field of the earth; and Cox, and others of the U.S. Geological Survey, have shown that the direction of magnetization in rocks from all over the world does in fact reverse itself at fairly regular intervals of the order of a million years. This observation is strikingly illustrated in Figs. 52 and 53.

Now Vine and Matthews find that the magnetic anomalies of the ocean floor east and west of the Atlantic Ridge in latitude 45°N are a kind of tape-recording of the recurrent reversals of the earth's field, as can be seen in Fig. 51. Thus the age of the ocean floor increases with increasing distance from the Atlantic Ridge, in startling agreement with the speculations of Robert Dietz of San Diego in California. For Dietz supposes that an ocean floor which is effectively composed of metamorphosed mantle rock, carried by the convection currents which diverge right and left below the mid-ocean rifts, spreads laterally as far

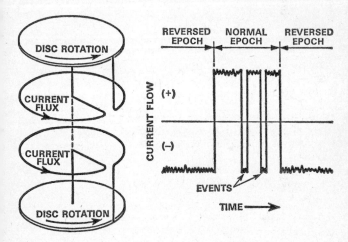

Fig. 52. A (two-disc) Faraday dynamo reproduces faithfully the behaviour of the earth's dipole field. (After Matthews and Gardiner.)

as the neighbouring continental shelves; where it slides downwards below the continental rafts, leaving its sediments plastered to the under-surface of each, like crumbs swept out of sight under the carpet.

The distribution of the sediments themselves over the Atlantic floor spells out the same tale. Thus the investigation of the Lamont group, carried out in the Atlantic during the 1963 season with their latest development of seismic shooting at sea – the so-called 'continuous profiler' – tells that in the region of the Mid-Atlantic Ridge the thickness of the sediments is rarely more than a few hundred metres and that frequently the bottom is as bare of sediment as the cliff illustrated in Plate 3; while the thickness increases with increasing distance from the continental shelf, until it is too great to be penetrated even by the powerful sonic beam of the Lamont profiler.

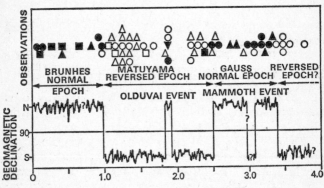

O NORTH AMERICA   TIME IN MILLIONS OF YEARS

□ EUROPE

△ HAWAII   CLOSED SYMBOLS: NORMAL POLARITY

▽ AFRICA   OPEN SYMBOLS: REVERSED POLARITY

Fig. 53. Crustal rocks show reversals in the direction of magnetization induced by the earth's field approximately every million years. The figure displays the magnetic polarities of sixty-four volcanic rocks, together with their potassium-argon ages. Note the sporadic 'events' – rapid reversals and re-reversals, which take only a few tens of thousands of years to accomplish. From Cox, Doell and Dalrymple: *Science*, vol. 144, pp. 1537–43, 26 June 1964.

THE ARCTIC BASIN

A last detail of the penultimate phase of earth's restless surface topography – the north polar land mass of $n = 4$ in Fig. 40.

The geological evidence points to the west Arctic as a sunken continent, and not a true ocean floor at all. Thus the floor of the western basin is covered with an exceptionally thick layer of sediment, in contradistinction to that of the world ocean. Moreover, two Arctic ridges show none of the mantle-borne characteristics of the great ocean ridges of Fig. 37: the Lomonosov Ridge, discovered by Soviet scientists in 1948, appears as a folded system of sedimentary strata; while the Alpha Ridge, traced from a United States drifting ice station during the IGY, is revealed as an intrusion of upthrust crystalline rocks. And both formations are dated as Mid-Mesozoic.

THE PACIFIC BASIN

Let us now turn to the Pacific, and in the first place to the recent discovery and exploration by H. W. Menard of 'Scripps' of the East Pacific Rise (Fig. 54).

The East Pacific Rise is a great hump in the ocean floor lying to the west of the Americas. It displays youthful features characteristic of other ocean-bottom ridges; the ocean floor over the rise is hot; gravity observations reveal a thin crust-cover; the sub-surface rocks are young semi-molten basalts with low seismic velocities. It is atypical in having no rift valley along its crest; an indication that it arose as an upward thrust of the ocean floor rather than as a corollary of continental fission.

If we follow the course of the Rise from south to north, we observe first two spurs, one seismic, the other aseismic, trending towards the west coast of South America; the Andean uplift is most probably a consequence of their eastward lunge.

Next, we observe the Rise *underthrusting* the Gulf of California; hence the high Colorado Plateau, which indeed has many of the characteristics of the crest of a mid-ocean ridge – high heat-flow to the surface, anomalous mantle velocity, unusually thin crust.

The lower western flank of the Rise appears once again seaward of the continental shelf off the Californian coast north of San Francisco; the crest emerges from under the continental raft northward of Cape Mendocino, whence it can be traced all the way to the Aleutians.

In general, echo-sounding reveals that the whole floor of the north-west Pacific slopes to the west, as the seaward flank of the East Pacific Rise.

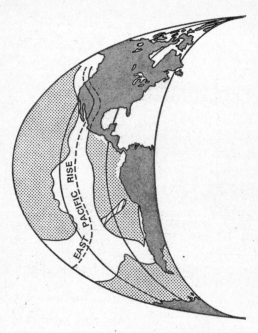

Fig. 54. The East Pacific Rise. (After Heezen.)

The area of the ocean bottom off Cape Mendocino has been mapped for its magnetic characteristics by Vacquier and his colleagues from 'Scripps'. The beautiful pattern which they obtained of the total intensity of magnetization of the basalt floor is shown in Fig. 55 – now recognized to be a pattern of magnetic reversals, such as those identified by Vine and Matthews on either side of the Mid-Atlantic Ridge.

An important practical feature of these magnetic patterns is that with them as guide it is possible to measure *the total lateral displacement* along the line of three transcurrent faults; and the answer can be as high as 1,000 miles.

Vacquier goes a little further, and questions the *rate* of slippage along the fault lines. This turns out to be of the order

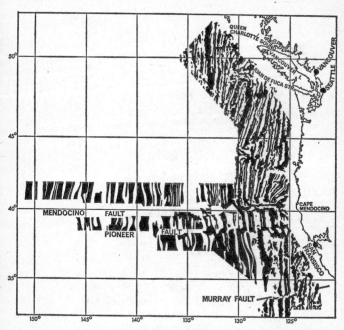

Fig. 55. Magnetic reversals in the floor of the East Pacific, as revealed by the ship's magnetometer of the Scripps expedition under Vacquier.

of 1 cm a year – of the same order, that is, as the speed of drift of the fragments of Gondwanaland north from the Antarctic circle, of Laurasia from the line of the Equator, and of the rate of spreading of the floor of the Atlantic. There is a strong possibility, however, that the transcurrent faults in the floor of the north-west Pacific broke *before* the formation of the East Pacific Rise.

In the south Pacific the influence of that sector of the mid-ocean ridge which springs southward from the centre of the Indian Ocean to circle Antarctica (Fig. 37) makes itself felt in the great transcurrent fault of New Zealand, which is in line with a spur of the mid-ocean ridge, in close analogy to the case of the San Andreas fault and East Pacific Rise.

Then there are the transcurrent faults associated with the sunken Melanesian Plateau (Fig. 56) explored among others by Rhodes Fairbridge of Columbia in New York; likewise with the remarkably linear trenches of Tonga and Kermadec. The system of lateral forces which sheared the crust to create these features must obviously have been extremely complicated, and no easy answer to the question of their origin can be looked for. However, Runcorn put forward some suggestions at the Royal Society of London's 1964 symposium on Continental Drift which are relevant to this problem. He draws attention to the fact that the spherical harmonic analysis of convection currents, up to the eighth harmonic, duly predicts a zone of compression off the Tonga Trench. Moreover, analysis of the gravity field to the third harmonic applies longitudinal tractions to the crust in a northerly direction at 10°S, which, if the corresponding axial gravity field were generalized, could demand in addition an east-west zone of tension in the latitude of 40–50°S. Within these limits of latitude lies the Melanesian Plateau; and the resultant tractions are in surprisingly good harmony with the shear stresses required to produce the actual system of trans-current faults.

Now look again at Fig. 56, and pinpoint the submerged tongue of land trending south-east from off New Caledonia towards New Zealand. Named the Lord Howe Rise, it is no isolated geological feature, but rather part of the New Zealand continental land-mass, large areas of which are likewise below sea level.

In Permo-Jurassic times this now continentalized land-mass was part of Western Antarctica: as an island-arc system lying off the Australian coast. Like its parent Archipelago it is young on the geological time-scale: its oldest rocks are at most 1,000 million years of age, as compared with the 3,000-million-year-old lavas of the Australia-Antarctic continental shield.

So the youthful New Zealand wandered north-eastward as

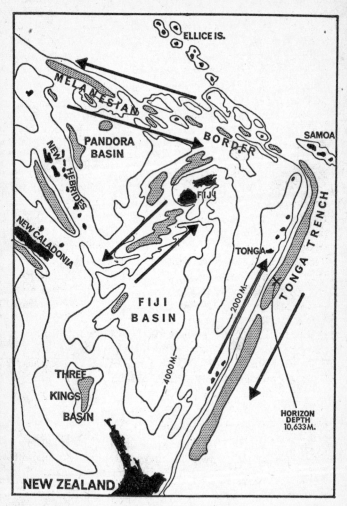

Fig. 56. Shear-faults in the sunken Melanesian Plateau, evidence of the current unrest in the earth's crust. (After Fairbridge.)

lonely as a cloud, until it came up against the basement of the Melanesian sub-continent. Then, in the penultimate geological era, namely the Tertiary, there formed off-shore the Tonga-Kermadec trench system and its recently discovered southern extension, the Hikurangi Trench that runs along the eastern edge of South Island. And finally came the inevitable uplift

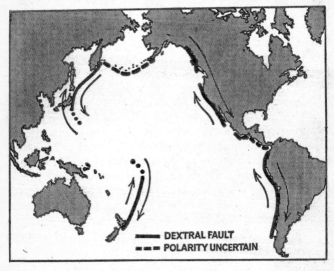

Fig. 57. Transcurrent faults on the borders of the Pacific. (After Benioff.)

landwards in the shape of the Southern Alps, one of the youngest mountain ranges in the world. . . . So there, maybe all too briefly, you have it.

The paleontological evidence, as advanced by Charles Fleming of the New Zealand Geological Survey, falls nicely into line with this surmise: for he shows that the flora and fauna of New Zealand were all but identical with those of Australia in the Jurassic, indigenous ever since the mid-Cretaceous page was turned. (See Fig. 45.)

Finally, there is the system of shoreline trans-current faults which encircle the Pacific (Fig. 57), indicating that the entire Pacific basin is twisting anti-clockwise relative to the surrounding land masses: as if a decoupling of the ocean-bottom crust from that of the continents were in progress in this area. Such a decoupling at work in the Pacific Basin, as distinct from the Atlantic Ocean, seems to be a natural enough corollary to Robert Dietz's ideas about spreading of the ocean bottom. For in the Atlantic there is indeed a continental carpet for the sediment crumbs to be swept under, to be plastered on its ventral aspect, maintaining isostatic equilibrium despite the losses of erosion on the dorsal. But at the edge of the Pacific the ocean floor plunges into the mantle at the chasmic barrier of the ocean trenches, whereby isostasy is looked after, not by the lost sediments, but by the volcanic uplift of the island arcs.

We are reminded here that the adjustment of the earth's crust to the final pattern on land and sea, called for by the final phase $n = 5$ of Fig. 40, may still be under way, and that it may not be complete for another fifty million years at least. We and our descendants must be prepared for a restless crust and mantle, turning and twisting like a dog upon the hearth, before he settles down to sleep. The contemporary catastrophes in Persia, Morocco, Chile, Yugoslavia, and Usbek may well be part of this story of the final adaptation of the earth's crust to the ultimate pattern of convection cells in the mantle.

CHAPTER FIVE

Sea and Sky

IN the three preceding chapters we have surveyed the evolution of the continental blocks of the earth's crust, and the changing topography of the ocean bottom; we have recognized two great fracture lines in the earth's crust – that of the mountain arcs a zone of compression, that of the mid-ocean rift a zone of tension; we have seen how these are most probably the outward and visible signs of the inward and invisible convection currents in the mantle, and how these convection currents directed the continents to their present stations and shaped the ocean basins as we know them today.

But the predominant role of the mantle in determining the earth's surface features doesn't end there: the air we breathe and the water we sail upon are also its offspring. All the water in the ocean was once volcanic steam; the earth's atmosphere – four parts nitrogen to one of oxygen – was once the ammonia, methane, and carbon dioxide belched forth from the world's volcanoes in Pre-Cambrian times.

Take the water first. The old story ran that torrents of rain fell upon the earth as it cooled and shrank from its pristine state as a fiery ball under a black sky – the tale of the puckered orange skin and the super-saturated atmosphere, in fact. Such a picture of past events is of course flatly contradicted by our present knowledge, namely that the composition of proto-earth was originally that of its parent sun, but that it *lost* almost all of its primeval atmosphere, and that in two distinct stages: first because the new broom of the young sun swept it away into outer space, some 5,000 million years ago; second because the lighter components of its remaining gases got shot off like slugs from a catapult, around 4,500 million years ago, from the spinning atmospheric bulge at the Equator, which was then rotating perhaps nearly ten times as fast as it is today, when proto-earth's youthful speed of rotation has been slowed down to its present middle-aged pace by the tidal drag of the moon. This second phase we know about because the quantities of such primeval gases as neon and krypton present today in the earth's atmosphere are only one hundred thousand millionth and one tenth of a millionth respectively of the proportional amounts present in the sun. No, Noah's flood came considerably later in the march of time.

However, if we compare the amount of water vapour emitted by all the volcanoes in the world since the beginning of geological time with the total volume of water present in the oceans, just as we did for the lavas and solid continents in Chapter 2, then we find that the two figures tally tolerably well at five million million cubic feet. Moreover, the *composition* of sea water points to a volcanic origin: its content of chlorides in particular – its saltiness, in other words – would be difficult to account for except as arising from the solution of the hydrochloric acid gas which accompanies the other gaseous hydrides in the eruption of lava from volcanoes.

Next, the atmosphere. The gases spewed out by volcanoes are predominantly *hydrides*, molecules of a small variety of chemical elements – nitrogen, carbon, oxygen – combined with hydrogen.

The production of the nitrogen and oxygen of our present-day atmosphere, therefore, was a *secondary* process, brought about by the photochemical decomposition of ammonia and water vapour by ultra-violet radiation coming from the sun: whereby the light mobile hydrogen atoms and hydrogen molecules escaped into outer space, leaving the heavier oxygen and nitrogen entrapped in the gravitational field of the earth. The methane fraction, too, would be photochemically decomposed; leaving behind carbon, ready to combine with the newly born oxygen to form CO_2.

Now the rate of production of oxygen from water vapour by the ultra-violet radiation from the sun is much too slow to convert to carbon dioxide *all* the carbon monoxide which has been pouring out into the atmosphere, since the beginning of geological time, from all the volcanoes of the world. It is clear that until this conversion was complete, any free oxygen in the atmosphere soon found itself imprisoned in a molecule of CO_2.

So on this basis there could be no free oxygen in the earth's atmosphere *until there were plants on the earth's surface to releas?* *it.* In other words, the air we breathe today is itself a product of living organisms, in addition to those products arising from the purely mechanical process of volcanic action beneath the earth's crust.

The earth's atmosphere and oceans, then, are as much a part of the earth we live on as its solid crust. Together they function as one great heat engine, powered by the sun, that conditions climate and weather, ocean waves and currents. The horse-power of the ocean-atmosphere heat engine is prodigious – two thousand million million horse-power. Its working fluid is water vapour, the winds of heaven its moving parts, the slow circulation of the oceans in their basins its massive flywheel.

Besides, the planetary heat engine is equipped with a colossally powerful 'feed-back' mechanism – its 'governor' in other words. No sooner does it begin to run too fast than restraining in-fluences immediately leap into operation: too slow, and accelerat-ing agents take over.

This all-important characteristic of the circulation cycles of atmosphere and oceans is at once a pedagogic headache and a mathematical nightmare; for the question it poses, alike to the expositor and the back-room boy who is struggling to understand them, is always the same: Where shall we begin?

Now the myriad readers of that admirable author Somerset Maugham know full well that all stories should be like those he could write best himself: they should have a beginning, a middle, and an end. Unfortunately, the blueprint of the planetary heat engine is inscribed on a cylinder – you can begin reading it any-where you like. As George Deacon, Director of the British National Institute of Oceanography, has put it: 'Do the trade winds give rise to the Gulf Stream, or is the Gulf Stream re-sponsible for the trade winds?'

So in the sequel, in which we shall meet this difficulty time and time again, it is well to remember that reading about climate and weather, winds and waves, is rather like a first attempt at understanding the philosophy of Immanuel Kant, which beginners are often warned they can only apprehend as a complete whole. . . .

The power house of the atmospheric heat engine is the sun. Each minute the sun radiates energy equivalent to the output of an electric heater rated at one billion quadrillion kilowatts. The earth intercepts but a small fraction (a circular sample of area πr_e^2, where r_e is the earth's radius) of this enormous total – about ten billionths, to be exact. This catch is distributed in virtue of the rotation of the earth over the earth's spherical surface of $4\pi r_e^2$: so that the initial input of solar radiation at the boundary of the earth's atmosphere is effectively reduced to one quarter of its incident value. Nevertheless, there remains 1.6×10^{15} kilowatts, or if you like 2×10^{15} horse-power, to drive the winds and the waves, to evaporate sea water to give us rain, to disintegrate the exposed rocks of mountain peaks and glacial shields, to pulverize the soil of the plains and valleys, to maintain the photosynthetic life of all plants, and to set in motion through photosynthesis by the microscopic algae in the surface waters of the oceans – the 'grass' or the sea pastures – the many-linked chain of life in the waters under the earth: herbivorous sub-microscopic diatoms and radiolaria, flesh-eating shrimps and copepods, small breeds of squids, and finally edible fishes like cod, halibut and tunny.

Now it is clear that the earth must radiate this captured energy back into space at exactly the same rate at which it receives it, otherwise the temperature of the earth would not be maintained at the steady average level we recognize as our world climate. This comes about through a rather complicated mechanism, conditioned by four chief factors: the oxygen in the upper atmosphere, the ozone layer that lies some 15 miles high above earth, the earth's cloud cover, and the presence throughout the lower reaches of the atmosphere of water and carbon dioxide in the proportions of 2 per cent and 3 hundredths of a per cent respectively.

The role of both the high-level oxygen content and the ozone layer of the upper atmosphere in the present context is very similar: put briefly, they absorb almost completely all electro-magnetic radiation from the sun shorter in wavelength than one hundred thousandth of an inch. Expressed rather more fully, this means that the energy in the ultra-violet end of the sun's spectrum which arrives at the top of the atmosphere is entirely expended: first, in the ionization of the high-lying oxygen, thus helping to form the ionosphere, the reflector of man-made radio-waves; second, in the photochemical decomposition of tri-atomic oxygen, ozone (O_3), into ordinary oxygen (O_2) and atomic oxygen (O).

Now studies of the ionosphere, or of the queer chemistry of the upper atmosphere, are outside the scope of this book. But we note here that it is not only the oxygen we breathe that makes life on earth as we know it possible; for a hundred miles high in the rarefied ionosphere and 15 miles high in the ozone layer it filters out the lethal shorter ultra-violet rays from the sun, only yielding passage to the longer ultra-violet rays, the kind which give us that Riviera sun-tan.

The effect of the clouds is very simple. Anyone who has looked down on them from an air-liner knows how white they are as seen from above. In the language of physics, they are tolerably efficient reflectors of the light incident upon them: to be exact, they are responsible for no less than 25 per cent of the total outgoing radiation from the earth.

What of the remaining 75 per cent? Close on 10 per cent is 'back-scattered' – from water droplets, dust particles, the very molecules of the air itself. The remaining 65 per cent goes out through a tiny little skylight in the earth's greenhouse without glass.

This is where the water vapour and carbon dioxide in the earth's atmosphere play their part. Both are transparent to the visible radiation from the sun, but together are very nearly opaque to all but a small portion of the infra-red region of the spectrum.

Now the narrow wave-band, lying almost solely in the visible part of the sun's spectrum, which actually strikes the earth's surface, land and sea alike, as approximately half of the total solar radiation incident at the top of the atmosphere, warms the land and the upper skin of the oceans so that they radiate, like any warm object, not in the visible but in the infra-red.

But only in the narrow region lying between the absorption bands of water vapour and carbon-dioxide can the infra-red radiation of the sun-warmed earth escape back into space. Here then is your 'greenhouse effect', the thermal regulator if you like, which ultimately sets the average temperature of the earth, and holds it at a steady world average over the years.

It is well at this point to stress the words 'world average value'; for clearly there are local fluctuations about that average, both seasonal and latitudinal: it is only the overall figure of the earth's surface temperature which gives a steady reading on the planetary thermometer.

This is well shown in Fig. 58, where the daily insolation, in arbitrary units 0 to 6, is plotted against latitude vertically and through the four seasons horizontally. We may read many important statements in this graphical expression of thousands of careful measurements. Thus:

1. The polar caps reflect almost all the solar radiation falling on them; in fact, during the Arctic and Antarctic winters they are practically perfect reflectors;

2. The heavy cloud cover over the Equator reflects so strongly that the areas of maximum insolation lie not on the geographical Equator, but to the north and south of it;

3. The areas of maximum insolation north and south of the Equator are not symmetrically located – insolation is more intense in the sub-tropical regions *south* of the Equator, because of the vastly greater area of poorly reflecting ocean water, as against that of the better reflecting land masses, which is a characteristic of the geography of the southern hemisphere.

We recognize in Fig. 58 the boiler and condenser of the atmospheric heat engine; namely the sub-tropical seas and the ice-caps over the poles. Thus a transfer of high-grade heat must be looked for from the Equator to the poles, the return of low-grade heat from the poles to the Equator: the 'steam' and 'condenser water' in fact of the familiar steam engine.

Now we have already stated baldly that the working fluid of the ocean-atmosphere heat engine is water vapour. How then is the heat engine fuelled? Answer: by the trade-wind clouds. Anyone who has voyaged from London to the Cape, or from

New York to Rio, has spent many peaceful hours watching the cloud galleons of the Trades as they sail before the wind, at first south, a week later towards the north, but always towards the Equator. Few realize that they are large-scale fuel pumps, raising water evaporated from the surface of the sea – in the northern hemisphere in the Caribbean or off Cape Verde, in the southern hemisphere off Porto Alegre and Walvis Bay – injecting it high into the warm air stream of the Trades.

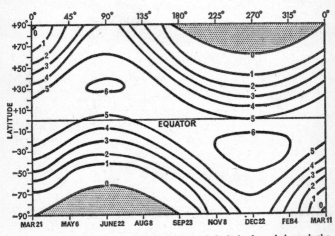

Fig. 58. Variations in the daily insolation both in latitude and through the four seasons of the year. (After Hauritz.)

The trade-wind clouds, in fact, are launched in the areas of maximum insolation depicted in Fig. 58. In these warm sub-tropical seas, the air above the water is particularly dry, for a good reason which will be made clear in the sequel. Straight-forward evaporation of water vapour from the surface of the ocean into the ambient air is therefore here at a maximum.

Water vapour crosses the sea/air interface, however, but rarely in a simple evaporation process from a flat surface, as in an inland lake. The rapid evaporation of spray, thrown up by the trade-winds themselves, has come to be recognized as a very important factor in the transfer of water vapour from oceans to atmosphere. Moreover, the *rate* of evaporation waxes and wanes with the roughly mondial cycle of the growth and decay of sub-tropical anticyclones, in tune with the meanderings of the polar jet-stream which we shall meet in the sequel: for when these sub-tropical anticyclones are at the peak of their development, the surface flow of the Trades becomes intense; and the air they transport is more than particularly dry, as it invariably is in a region of high pressure. In short, conditions are then at their optimum for rapid evaporation.

Thus the injection of water vapour into the working cycle of the atmospheric heat engine takes place in spurts, spaced fairly regularly at intervals of from three to five weeks. The trade-wind clouds, in other words, visit always the same filling stations, but are not invariably supplied with the same number of gallons. And you can actually see this reflected in their shape and form: now small and stunted, now towering giants (see Plate 20).

But whatever the mechanism and rate of evaporation of water vapour from the ocean may be, one constant physical process rules throughout: namely, that not only must the temperature of the water be raised to the evaporation point by the heat of the sun, but an *additional* amount of heat must be injected – the so-called *latent heat of evaporation* – as when we bring a domestic kettle to the boil. It is in fact the latent heat of evaporation in sea water, later released into the upper atmosphere, which is the source of energy that drives the planetary winds (and ocean currents, as we shall see in due course) just as in the familiar steam engine.

A certain fraction of the total amount of latent heat transferred from sea to air over the sub-tropical seas goes to drive the fuel pumps of the trade-wind clouds themselves. Studies from specially equipped aircraft of the tall chimney-shaped clouds have shown that they are in a constant state of growth, mostly to windward, with a corresponding secular decay down wind: giving rise to a turbulent circulation within each cloud which pumps water vapour upwards from the intake near sea-level to the output at a height of 7,000 feet or more. In their passage to the Equator, either from the north or from the south, the trade-wind clouds constantly inject enormous quantities of water vapour, night and day, into the ever-warmer air stream of the Trades.

Arrived at the Equator, the warm moist air from the north converges with the trade-winds of the southern hemisphere, and is swept aloft, carrying the clouds with it. In its ascent to the cold regions of the higher atmosphere, its water vapour is jettisoned, to fall in sheets of tropical rain on land and sea below. At the same time, the solar energy it has held entrapped as latent heat during its journey south is released, to drive the whole planetary wind system.

Let us follow now the track of the trade-winds from their starting points 30° north or south of the Equator. They begin as winds driving due south or due north, as the case may be, from the dry areas of high pressure in the Horse Latitudes. Gradually however they alter course, from due south to south-west or from due north to north-west; for they are winds which must obey the deflecting force of a spinning earth – the so-called 'Coriolis force' about which we shall soon learn. Converging at the Equator, they are forced to sweep vertically upwards, until at 20,000 feet or so above earth they find themselves constituting a girdle around the earth of air at relatively high pressure. Thence, they spread north and south in a complex pattern of swirls and eddies, until they come against the sub-tropical jet streams, high up under the roof of the earth's lower atmosphere – the so-called troposphere. Here the air is cold, dry and heavy; it sinks earthward to resume the cycle, east of the Bermudas or south of the Canaries as the case may be.

We have traced the boundaries of the *trade-wind cells*, sometimes called the Hadley cells after their discoverer George Hadley, eighteenth-century British astronomer, the circulation in which is *meridianal* (see Plate 22).

Contrary to the chart of the planetary winds drawn up in the days of sail, which proposed two further meridianal circulation cells in each hemisphere to account for the westerlies in the north and south temperate zones and the prevailing easterlies within the Arctic and Antarctic Circles, the air age now recognizes the trade-wind cell as the only example of straight meridianal circulation in the earth's atmosphere. For north of 30°N and south of 30°S the winds blow *zonally* in two great vortices around the poles as centre.

Let us concentrate our attention for the moment on the northern system, lying between latitudes 80°N and 30°N, at an average height of 20,000 feet.

Fig. 59. The chart of the planetary winds current in the days of sailing ships, which showed three separate meridianal circulation cells in each hemisphere. The air age recognizes only the trade-wind cells as valid; north and south of these, zonal circulation predominates.

The core of the north polar vortex of winds is the polar jet stream, discovered in latitude 60°N during the Second World War by high-flying long-distance bombers of the U.S. Air Force. The polar jet stream is no tame river of air: it is a rushing mighty wind, concentrated in an aerial funnel only 300 miles wide and 3 miles high, roaring around the roof of the world with a speed of 200 m.p.h. or more at a height of 30,000 feet above ground. Its influence is felt down as far as 10,000 feet, the lower limit of the so-called geostrophic winds that trace out the great circles of the globe between the Arctic Circle and 30°N.

But wait a bit! Are we going too fast and too far? Is the jet stream indeed Prospero commanding, or is he rather obedient Ariel running his master's errands on the sharp winds of the north? Here indeed we are squarely faced with the feed-back riddle; and we can only answer that it's true either way, but that the way we've put it is fair enough for didactic purposes.

That word of warning having been given, let us proceed.

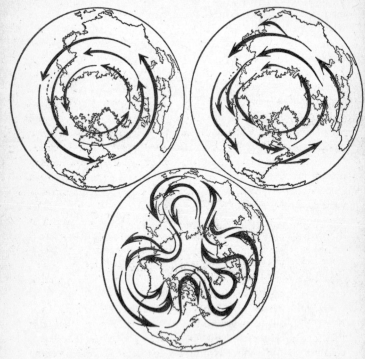

Fig. 60. Three stages in the breakdown of the geostrophic phase of the polar jet stream. In the final stage, a turbulent exchange of hot and cold air between the subtropics and the north polar region is effected, which goes to assure the transport of heat from the Equator to the Pole, and its return, downgraded, to the Equator: a cycle which must be maintained if the atmospheric heat engine is to be kept steadily in motion.

Faced with a *zonal* circulation of winds aloft, centred on the polar jet stream, how can we account for the interchange of warm and cold air (so majestically achieved in the trade-wind meridianal cell between Equator and 30°N), between 30°N and the Pole?

The answer comes as the result of an intensive experimental and theoretical investigation, carried out during the forties of the present century under the inspired direction of one man – Carl Gustav Rossby, hard-living, hard-working Swede who burned himself out to die in 1957 at the age of fifty-nine.

And here is his answer: The polar jet stream is a black sheep, unlike its brothers, the sub-tropical jet streams above the Horse Latitudes, which pursue their even way around the world year in and year out. As much as a month at a time, the polar jet stream behaves as any well-conducted geostrophic wind should, obeying the eastward spin of the earth, piling up pressure to the right of its direction of motion, holding to its circular track about the Pole. But at intervals of three to five weeks, sometimes even longer, intervals which are meantime unpredictable to man, it breaks loose. It lashes itself into great loops, 4,000 miles or more across, dragging the whole circumpolar vortex with it, thrusting cold air from the north south to the tropics, hauling warm air north from the Caribbean. And it is in this untidy way of Fig. 60 that the interchange of warm and cold air between the sub-tropics and the polar regions is accomplished.

This Walpurgisnacht in the upper atmosphere is staged between 10,000 and 30,000 feet. What of the corresponding conditions near the earth's surface?

To those of us who live along the eastern borders of the North Sea, this is a very pertinent question. For the answer is this: During a period of rebellion on the part of the jet stream, cold dry air lying above Northern Canada can be pulled southward behind the trough of an eastward advancing wave in the scalloped edge of the polar vortex, warm air from the Caribbean can be sucked into the rearward edge of the next northward-probing crest. The two air masses meet in a turbulent struggle on the western seaboard of the Atlantic – and the birth of a whole family of cyclones is announced on the lower slopes of the polar vortex.

And in due course the separate members of the cyclone family leave the parental hearth: circular currents of air flowing against the clock, they drift eastward across the Atlantic as the 'depressions' which the western European knows only too well. . . .

So much for zonal circulation in the atmosphere polewards of 30°N. Now for 'hot news' from Antarctica.

Next to nothing was known about the atmosphere of Antarctica before that *annus mirabilis* 1957, the year of the IGY, when no fewer than twelve national expeditions wintered in Antarctica, intent on the scientific exploration of an area of the earth's surface nearly twice as large as Australia. The moving spirit in the meteorological programme was the late Harry Wexler, Chief of the U.S. Meteorological Service, who died suddenly in the spring of 1962 at the early age of 51. He left behind him a noble monument to his unique drive and professional skill in the clear picture we now have of the south polar vortex.

No one expected to find a replica of Rossby's polar vortex in the south. In the north, the conditions aloft are influenced by the enormous land masses of North America and northern Eurasia, and by the all but landlocked Arctic Ocean; as also by the unstable thermal equilibrium above the Caribbean. Antarctica, on the other hand, is bounded by the Southern Ocean: apart from the tip of South America, the nearest land mass – Australia – is upwards of 10,000 miles distant from the South Pole. The Antarctic Ocean current, unlike the ocean gyres we shall meet later in the ocean basins, encircles Antarctica as one fast-flowing west-east current in latitude 45°S.

And as the outcome of eight years of intensive study, centred on the United States 'Weather Central' by the Ross Sea, but carried out by a combined team of American, French, Russian and British Commonwealth citizens, there emerges a comparatively simple pattern of zonal circulation aloft, and of the 'ventilation' (to use Harry Wexler's evocative expression) of the south polar vortex by winds from the north.

The mid-winter circulation high aloft over Antarctica is one of strong westerly winds circling an area of low pressure over the pole, to be replaced in the Antarctic summer by a high when the warming of the upper atmosphere by the twenty-four-hour day sun is complete. There is none of the instability of the north-polar jet stream in the south, no sporadic cut-offs of masses of air south and north. The core of the Antarctic vortex, the south-polar jet stream, is a true geostrophic wind all the year round.

During the Antarctic winter, strong cyclonic storms sweep the lower reaches of the high-lying Antarctic plateau, which, however, never penetrate to the centre of the Antarctic continent. Since cyclones in the southern hemisphere spiral clockwise under the action of the Coriolis force (see Fig. 64), these storms sweep in the same sense about the pole as does the south

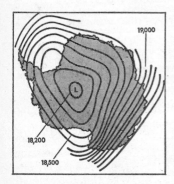
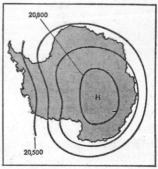

Fig. 61. Circumpolar circulation, winter and summer, approximately 20,000 metres, or 65,000 feet, above the Antarctic continent.

polar vortex: consequently, violent turbulence in the upper reaches of the atmosphere is here absent.

The origin of these storms lies far to the north, around latitude 30°S, where gigantic sub-tropical cyclones (rotating clockwise) form over the warm ocean, to sail south before the westerlies of the southern hemisphere. These cyclones, warm and wet, transport heat and water vapour to Antarctica, which would otherwise be starved of both. Tiros IV, Wexler's 'weather eye', caught one of them making south on 18 May 1962 (see Plate 21).

The cold dry air over the Antarctic plateau is carried coastward by the so-called 'katabatic winds" which are such a marked feature of Antarctic weather. They flow downwards over the slopes which form the outer zone of the continental land mass at a speed of 20 knots or more. This shoreward flow is normally quite smooth; but it can become suddenly turbulent, and trigger the dreaded Antarctic blizzard, if the speed of flow exceeds a certain critical value appropriate to the local terrain.

Our sketch of the south polar vortex, and of the simple mechanism of its ventilation in the exchange of cold dry air for air that is warm and wet, is complete. . . .

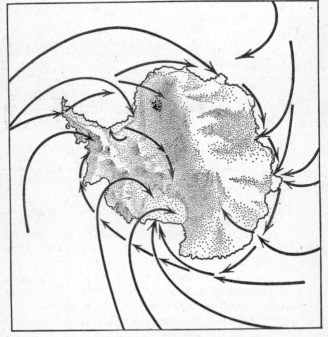

Fig. 62. Winter storms in Antarctica.

It all began with the trade-wind clouds, and ended with the gigantic clockwise cyclone above Antarctica. But at the risk of being accused of an act of regurgitation, one is obliged to emphasize once again that the planetary wind field is a fenced-in paddock, that the music of the four winds goes round and round and comes out nowhere at all, that the feed-back controlling any one-directional mechanism in the set-up of the earth's atmosphere is so strong that a description of its general circulation could legitimately start with an account of the local weather conditions over the British Isles or the Jamaicas. The Tiros satellites, coupled more than fortunately with the advent of high-performance electronic computers, may well put a new complexion within our own lifetime on the whole complex mathematical and indeed didactic problem. But the time is not quite yet.

Fig. 63. From Munster's *Cosmographia* (New York Public Library).

The time *has* come, however, to review once more in this book the planetary wind system – but now in a more succinct analytical form, rather than in the former descriptive fashion, in which he who ran might read.

Thus we enter on our résumé with the effect of a spinning earth on every particle of air or water in the atmosphere or the oceans. Now the trade-winds, with which we began, are first launched from dry high-pressure areas in the Horse Latitudes, around 30° north and south of the Equator, as winds that are flowing due south or due north as the case may be. Quite quickly, however, they become the 'easterlies' of the northern and southern hemispheres, under the combined effect of the so-called *Coriolis force* and of the *frictional drag* of their passage over the air/sea interface.

Everybody who has held vigil with the fixed stars in the eastern sky on a summer's night in northern latitudes has seen the horizon sweeping beneath them in a left-hand turn: an observer in the southern latitudes sees it as a right-hand turn. In other words, the earth is spinning anti-clockwise within the primary frame of reference of the fixed stars; and so if we aim to describe with mathematical precision the motion of an object moving over the earth's surface, or through the air above it or under the water of the oceans, we must refer that motion to a system of co-ordinate axes held steady in the framework of the stars.

This idealized procedure can however become very cumber-

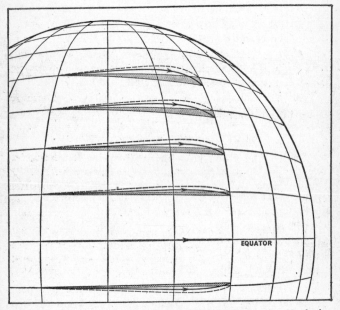

Fig. 64. The Coriolis force on a rocket projected horizontally towards the east, at four different latitudes in the northern hemisphere. The Coriolis force, acting to deflect the rocket to the right (or southward) of its direction of motion, decreases steadily with decreasing latitude to the value zero at the Equator.

some when describing the complex motions of the winds and the ocean currents, and so we have recourse to a trick invented by Gaspard Gustave de Coriolis away back in 1835: we pretend that the earth is at rest, and ascribe the observed trajectories of objects moving within the fixed frame of reference of the stars to an imaginary force, the Coriolis force, urging a particle moving horizontally to the earth's surface to change its direction of motion to one *at right angles* to its direction at any instant – towards the *right* in northern latitudes, towards the *left* in southern latitudes.

Moreover, the *strength* of the Coriolis force is a maximum at the poles, dropping with decreasing latitude to zero at the Equator: a statement that can be visualized rather easily by imagining a rocket to be projected horizontally, first due east or west at the North Pole, then due east or west at the Equator. In the first case our hypothetical rocket would appear to be strongly deflected towards the right; at the Equator it would sail over the horizon strictly in the line of fire.

That is the qualitative description. Quantitatively it can be put in the form of a simple mathematical equation.

Thus

$$C = (2.\omega_e.\sin\varphi)\,u = f.u$$

where C is the Coriolis force per unit mass, ω_e is the angular velocity of rotation of the earth, φ is the latitude, and u is the eastward component of the velocity of a particle of air or water relative to the earth; while the quantity $2\omega_e\sin\varphi = f$ is known as the *Coriolis parameter*.

Note that the argument which has been developed above for an east-west motion over the earth's surface applies equally to a north-south motion. Thus if v is the velocity of a particle toward the north, the Coriolis force C acting on it is f.v.

Thus the *easterlies* of the trade winds, both north and south of the Equator, are neatly accounted for. They are winds that started out equatorwards, but which have been deflected *to the right* in the northern latitudes, *to the left* in the southern: winds moreover that have been restrained from swinging through a right angle to their initial direction, to become *east winds* rather than *easterlies*, by the friction set up at the air/sea interface.

Clearly, the easterlies of the Trades are moving partly against the west-to-east rotation of the earth. Therefore in their frictional passage over land, but chiefly over the sea, they borrow a fraction of the rotational momentum of the spinning earth. This debt must be repaid, otherwise the whole general circulation of the atmosphere would grind to a stop.

This was first pointed out as late as 1926 by Harold Jeffreys of Cambridge, who in discovering the solution of the very difficult problem of *how* the stolen momentum is restored to its original possessor – the earth – builded better than he knew, as we shall see in a moment. Jeffreys began by considering not only the surface easterlies at the bottom of the trade-wind cycle, but also the surface westerlies (as distinct from the high-level polar vortices) which flow poleward north and south of the Horse Latitudes. These are winds which have a component moving *with* the rotation of the earth, and hence *part* with some of their own momentum in their passage poleward. Moreover, the frictional area of the earth's surface lying beneath the westerlies nicely balances that beneath the easterlies.

The problem is thus reduced to a single interrogation: What is the *mechanism* of the momentum exchange between the easterlies and the westerlies, required to restore the momentum balance over the whole system of earth and atmosphere, so that there is no net loss or gain to either? Jeffreys pointed out that this end can only be achieved by the turbulent mixing of air eddies high above ground across the boundary between the two systems.

Now comes the dramatic climax: for a mathematical analysis, more than somewhat abstruse, shows that such turbulent mixing is most readily achieved across a boundary for which the increase in wind velocity in a vertical direction is a maximum. And in the 1940s, not only were the required turbulent eddies aloft in the trade-wind cells actually observed by high-flying balloons and aircraft, but the sub-tropical jet streams were discovered, flowing under the roof of the atmosphere 30° north and south of the Equator, directly above the calms of the Horse Latitudes at sea level!

The conditions are very different in the polar vortices, for at 20,000 feet the frictional drag of the rotating earth is absent. The winds of the circumpolar whirls are essentially *geostrophic*, or 'earth-turned' winds, tracing out great circles over the globe high aloft – as indeed do the sub-tropical jet streams.

Geostrophic winds are born of two opposing forces: the

Coriolis force, and the so-called *pressure gradient force*. Taking the north-polar jet stream as a specific example – a wind blowing from west to east – we see at once that the Coriolis force is acting on it in a direction pointing due south. But as it whirls about the pole the particles of air in the stream are thrown southwards by centrifugal force, where they build up a higher pressure on the outer rim of the jet stream than on the inner rim, which is depleted of air particles by the same action of centrifugal force. In other words, a *pressure gradient* is established across the jet stream from south to north, such that the pressure gradient force directed due north exactly balances the Coriolis force directed due south. The jet stream during its quiescent periods is a true geostrophic wind.

In its periods of so-called 'meandering' (a weak word to describe the lashing of an aerial whip) the 4,000-mile-wide waves of the circumpolar vortex gave birth to families of *cyclones* along the eastern seaboard of North A erica, and calved isolated *anticyclones* over the sub-tropical seas. Let us take a closer look at these areas of low pressure and high pressure respectively – the 'lows' and 'highs' of the meteorologist.

The life history of the cyclones of the northern hemisphere was first written down in the early twenties by the Bergen school of meteorologists in Norway, under the inspiration of Vilhelm and Jakob Bjerknes, father and son. Twenty years before their most outstanding pupil, Carl Gustav Rossby, had unravelled the aerodynamics of the polar vortex, they argued that the typical depression of the temperate latitudes must begin as a *wave* at the boundary of two air streams, a cold dense air stream flowing south-east from the arctic circle, a warm light air stream flowing north-west from the sub-tropics.

In Fig. 65 is the world-famous diagram that Jakob Bjerknes and his pupil Harald Solberg drew in 1921, to explain the birth of the Western Atlantic cyclones.

In the final stage of the formation of a depression, all distinction between the parent air masses is lost: the depression detaches itself from the 'polar front' between the two air streams as a cyclone, a mass of air rotating anti-clockwise under the action of the Coriolis force of the spinning earth, circumscribed by winds which spiral inwards to the centre of the depression. The centre is cold, from its origins, and wet from the condensed water vapour of the warm air from the Caribbean, 'occluded' in the earlier stages of its formation.

The anti-cyclones of the northern latitudes have come north from the Azores, masses of dry air from aloft, warmed by compression as they descend from the upper atmosphere to the

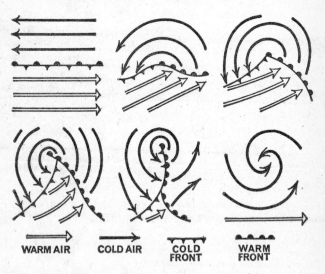

WARM AIR   COLD AIR   COLD FRONT   WARM FRONT

Fig. 65. The birth of a cyclone on the warm/cold 'front' off the east coast of North America.

barometric 'high' at sea level. As such, they are areas of high pressure: anti-cyclonic winds flow outwards from the centre of the 'high', spiralling clockwise under the action of the Coriolis force.

In the southern hemisphere, of course, the direction of rotation of cyclones and anti-cyclones is reversed. Cyclones in southern latitudes spiral *clockwise*, since the Coriolis force on the inflowing winds acts to the *left* of their direction of motion, instead of to the *right*, as in the northern hemisphere. By the same token, anti-cyclones in southern latitudes spiral *anti-clockwise*.

In all the above, the word 'cyclone' should not be confused with the words 'hurricane' or 'typhoon'. These horrid winds with the girls' names have quite another and indeed seemingly capricious origin.

In the jargon of the meteorologists, the flow of air in a hurricane or typhoon is described as 'cyclostrophic', in analogy with 'geostrophic'. In cyclostrophic motion the *centrifugal force*, acting outwards on the whirling mass of air, is balanced by the

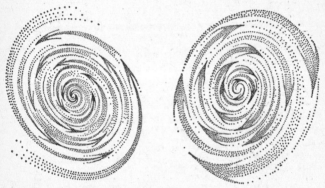

Fig. 66. Cyclone and anti-cyclone in the northern hemisphere.

pressure gradient force acting inwards. As the air in the hurricane ascends, it becomes less dense: hence the radius of the typhoon increases, as you can see in Fig. 67.

Cyclostrophic rotation is so violent that it is freed entirely from the Coriolis force of the rotating earth, although the *initial* sense of rotation of a nascent typhoon may be given to it by the larger scale flow in which it is embedded: thus the hurricanes that harry the east coast of the United States rotate predominantly anti-clockwise, the typhoons of the tropics predominantly clockwise, since their centres are alike areas of low pressure. . . .

So much for an analysis of the cyclostrophic flow of air within a fully formed and angrily active hurricane or typhoon. But what of the mechanism of parturition? What are the conditions which

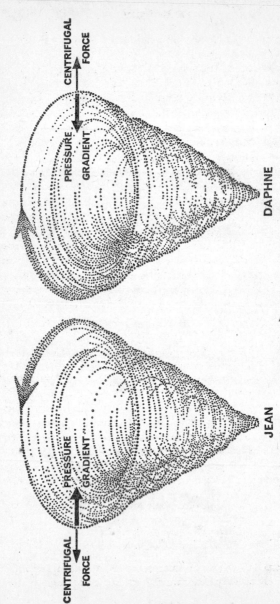

Fig. 67. Jean and Daphne, hurricane and typhoon, twisting counter-clockwise and clockwise respectively.

are necessary and sufficient for the birth of a Betsy or a Belinda – so called *cyclogenesis*?

Here the experts are somewhat at variance. Thus, to quote from the cautious text of a conflated account of the current status of our knowledge concerning the *Interaction between the Atmosphere and the Oceans*, issued in 1960 by the U.S. Academy of Sciences in Washington: 'Most meteorologists agree that local heat sources over the oceans may be an essential element in the origin and maintenance of cyclonic disturbances over the oceans . . . although in each instance the complete role of air-sea interaction is still unsolved. How and why do local anomalies in sea-surface temperature occur? Given an oceanic heat source, what are the mechanics and thermodynamics of the atmospheric reaction and the resultant 'feed-back' to the ocean itself?'

Then there is the 'do-it-yourself' approach of Mrs Joanne Starr Malkus of Woods Hole, who piloted the aircraft from which the astounding cloudscapes of Plate 20 were photographed. She says that the necessary condition for the formation of a hurricane within the highest of these towering clouds is the formation of a 'warm core', but that this condition is left necessary but not sufficient unless the core is 10° to 15°C above its surroundings. And she leaves it at that.

Richard Scorer, who is Professor of Theoretical Mechanics at Imperial College, London, has made a bold theoretical attack on the mechanics and thermodynamics of hurricane formation – and he may well have gone far towards solving the problem. His line of reasoning is, however, definitely unorthodox, and a short digression is indicated before we summarize the argument and conclusions he has set out in *Science Journal*, for March 1966.

The *orthodox* dogma concerning turbulence in gases is neatly epitomized by L. F. Richardson's celebrated jingle, which runs:

> Big whirls have little whirls
> Which feed on their velocity;
> Little whirls have lesser whirls
> And so on to viscosity;

which can, of course, be interpreted as a statement of the Second Law of Thermodynamics for a particular case.

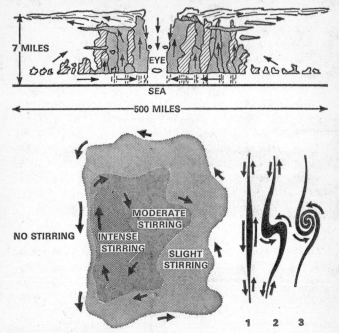

Fig. 68. Cyclogenesis. The upper drawing is the schematized profile of a typical hurricane; cumulus clouds tower around the eye, spreading laterally as they touch the roof of the tropopause, and thinning out with increasing distance from the axis (note that the vertical scale is exaggerated). The lower picture shows in cross-section how a vortex, chancily conceived by a warm core, can spin itself into a true hurricane. (Scorer.)

Scorer asserts that while a degradation of coordinated to un-coordinated fluid flow may be true in *general*, nevertheless a *local* 'flouting' of the Second Law is permissible. Here he is joined by Victor Starr and his group at M.I.T., who maintain that the behaviour even of the frontal cyclones illustrated in Fig. 66, which are of the order of 1,000 miles or so in diameter as compared with a mere 100 miles or so for a tropical hurricane, is difficult to account for except phenomenologically unless the big whirls are allowed to feed on the little ones. . . . All alike men with the courage of their convictions!

And here in brief is what Scorer is convinced of. He agrees with the general opinion that the birthplace of tropical hurricanes is in one of the so-called 'anvil clouds' which form before one's eyes from the cloud-towers of the Trades – you can pick out several such in the upper photograph of Plate 20. He agrees with Joanne Starr that a warm core to a chance vortex within an anvil cloud is a necessary condition for the vortex to spin into a true hurricane (like Rudi Nureyev when he swings his outstretched arms close to his body in a harlequin spin). But from then onwards his argument is unorthodox; he sums it up himself in a cheeky counter-jingle to L. F. Richardson's:

> The buoyant force of heat appears
> In clouds by condensation,
> And spreading out of rising airs
> Feeds larger scale rotation.

Now look at Fig. 68, with its caption, which will allow you to follow Scorer's argument to its conclusion.

*

Finally, let us review very briefly the concept of *vorticity*, so richly developed by Rossby, which we shall find quite indispensable in our later discussion of ocean currents.

Any volume of fluid at rest on the earth's surface anywhere but on the Equator is rotating in the fixed frame of reference of the stars, since there exists in all latitudes except zero latitude a local vertical component of the earth's rotation. Such a volume of fluid is said to possess 'planetary vorticity'. But there are many examples in meteorology and oceanography of a volume of air or water which has a tendency to spin around a vertical axis apart from that provided by the earth's rotation in space: such a volume of fluid possesses *relative vorticity* with respect to a fixed earth – and it is with such that we are chiefly concerned here.

Now relative vorticity can be changed either by a vertical stretching or shrinking of a column of the fluid (Fig. 69), or by a change of latitude (Fig. 70). Fig. 69 is self-explanatory; Fig. 70 needs some explanation. The barrel of viscous liquid which we may imagine with von Arx of Woods Hole to be carried from the North Pole by easy stages towards the Equator – very carefully, so as not to disturb its liquid contents – is at rest relative to the earth whenever we set it down. Not so the contents, which maintain the tendency to rotate anti-clockwise which they acquired from their container at the North Pole, *even when parked on the Equator*. On the other hand, if the barrel is carried north from the Equator, it will pick up the *planetary* vorticity appropriate to the local vertical, while the liquid contents remain at rest. But since anyone who took off the lid of the barrel to see how the contents were getting on would be rotating anti-clockwise around the local vertical along with the barrel, he would see the liquid rotating clockwise *relative to a fixed earth*.

The vorticity theory has been applied with striking success by Walter Munk of La Jolla in California to the wind-driven circulation of the surface currents of the world's ocean basins.

One glance at a world map of the surface currents of the oceans instantly reveals a consistent picture of clockwise rotation in the northern hemisphere, of counter-clockwise rotation in the southern hemisphere, of a geostrophic circulation ringing

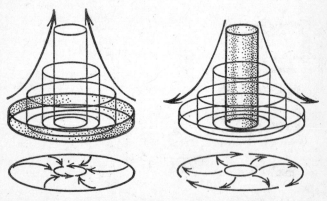

Fig. 69. Diagram showing how the relative vorticity of a column of fluid can be changed by vertical stretching or shrinking, giving rise to cyclonic motion of the fluid in the first case, anti-cyclonic motion in the second, under the action of the Coriolis force.

Antarctica. But look more closely and there emerges a pattern of non-symmetrical circulation in the ocean basins: the currents are invariably narrower and stronger *on the western shores* of the oceans. We recognize the Gulf Stream in the North Atlantic, the Brazil Current in the South Atlantic, the Kuro Shiwo Current off the Islands of Japan in the North Pacific.

Take the North Atlantic as a specific example. Here there is a gigantic anti-cyclone or clockwise gyre of surface currents, generated at the air/ocean interface by the cat's-paws that streak before the easterly Trades of the tropics and the westerlies of the middle latitudes. This ocean gyre would be symmetrical about a central point in the Atlantic were it not that the vertical water columns moving north in the western quarter of the ocean and south in the eastern quarter acquire clockwise and anti-clockwise vorticity respectively in their passage north and south: always

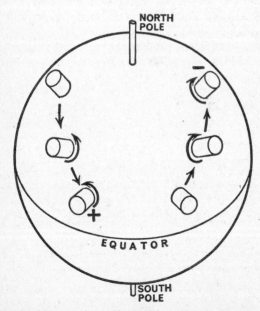

Fig. 70. Diagram showing the change of relative vorticity with latitude. (After von Arx.)

subject to the action of the Coriolis force, which increases in strength polewards, diminishes in strength equatorwards.

Thus the Coriolis force, acting to the right of the direction o motion in the North Atlantic, tends to *increase* the clockwise rotation of a column of water moving north along the eastern border of North America, and by the same token to *decrease* the rate of anti-clockwise rotation of a column moving south off the coast of Africa. Hence the influence of the Coriolis force alone would lead to an unlimited increase of the vorticity of the ocean gyre as a whole: and we must look for a feed-back mechanism which will restrain such a runaway system and ensure a condition of stable equilibrium.

Munk finds the needed brake in friction between the boundaries of the ocean gyre and the edges of the adjacent land masses. On the eastern side, the diminishing strength of the Coriolis force as the boundary of the gyre moves equatorward allows a slow broad drift southwards, without appreciable friction at the coast-line. On the western side, however, the increase in the strength of the Coriolis force, here aided by the tendency toward vertical shrinkage of a water column transported northward into

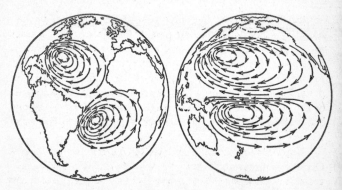

Fig. 71. The pattern of surface currents in the Atlantic and in the Pacific – ocean gyres rotating clockwise in the northern hemisphere, anti-clockwise in the south. The stark asymmetry of all four gyres springs to the eye, although they are the offspring of four tolerably symmetrical planetary windfields. Walter Munk of 'Scripps' has found an explanation of all this, which is set out fully in the text.

ever colder waters, acts to produce an always greater clockwise vorticity in a vertical water column as the current flows north, thus demanding a strong interaction with the coast. This leads to the production of a shearing force, opposing the current and inducing an anti-clockwise frictionally generated vorticity to balance that generated by the Coriolis force. Hence the strong narrow current of the Gulf Stream.

To sum up: a perfectly symmetrical planetary wind field, set up by the Trades and westerlies, has produced a strongly asymmetric ocean gyre in the surface waters of the North Atlantic, by a feed-back mechanism induced by that same rotation of the earth as gave rise to the Trades and westerlies. No wonder Deacon remarked that you might as well say that the Gulf Stream was as much responsible for the Trades as vice versa.

Look again at Fig. 71, in particular at the chart of the surface currents in the Pacific; and one distinguishes immediately a linear east-to-west surface current at the common boundary of the northern-hemisphere and southern-hemisphere ocean gyres, *which follows the line of the equator*. This is the Pacific Equatorial Current.

Now in September 1951, the late Townsend Cromwell, aboard a United States Fish and Wildlife Service research vessel, noticed that his long-line fishing gear was drifting below surface *to the east* – in the opposite direction that is to the surface equatorial current. This acute observation was immediately followed up, and by 1958 the existence was established of a well-defined counter-current moving from west to east with a velocity of 150 cm/sec, the core of which is located at a depth of around 100 metres. It has been named Cromwell Current in honour of its discoverer.

The precise analogue of the Cromwell Current for the Atlantic Ocean was discovered in the year 1959, by the Russian research vessel *Mikhail Lomonosov*, flowing right across the ocean below surface at a speed of 120 cm/sec; and in the summer of 1963 the Royal Research Ship *Discovery III* found the Indian Ocean equatorial counter-current, this time with the comparatively low speed of 60 cm/sec.

These shallow equatorial counter-currents are therefore a

feature common to the World Ocean. Oddly enough, they escaped the very extensive classical analysis of wind-driven surface currents made by the Swedish oceanographer Harald Sverdrup and his school, because they neglected to take account of the sub-surface frictional stresses set up by the motion of the surface water layers. When the mathematics is made to include such frictional terms, then shallow counter-currents are in fact duly predicted.

The next question is: How far below the surface does the *direct* influence of the atmosphere on the waters of the world ocean extend? The answer is always the same: a sharp vertical division of the ocean into an upper layer, of just over half a mile, wherein the water rapidly becomes both colder and less salty with depth; and a lower layer, in which temperature and salinity remain nearly constant all the way down to the ocean floor.

It is on this foundation that Henry Stommel, of Woods Hole Oceanographic Institute in New England, has developed his brilliant theory of the 'two-level ocean', which already carries the sign-manual of all good theories – it predicts the right results.

Stommel postulates a two-layer ocean, in which water from the upper layer sinks to the lower layer in the sub-arctic region, and rises from the lower to the upper layer in the sub-antarctic. He has not attempted so far to say why this should be so: in other words, his is essentially a 'phenomenological theory', in which careful analysis of a multitude of empirical data leads to an inspired guess – after which the argument is developed with strict attention to logic.

Pinpointing our attention now on the Atlantic, we should expect, on the two-layer theory, that the Arctic bottom water rises to the upper layer in the South Atlantic, opposite the coast of Argentina: a result which is actually in good agreement with a full analysis of the results of the *Discovery II* cruises in the southern seas in the years 1929–30.

The map at Fig. 73 shows two major features: first that below the Gulf Stream must flow a deep-sea counter-current; second, that the Brazil Current has no such deep-sea counter-current, and so to maintain equilibrium of the general circulation should be weaker than the Gulf Stream – which indeed it is.

In April 1957 the *Atlantis* from Woods Hole in New England and the *Discovery II* from the United Kingdom joined forces off the coast of Florida to search for Stommel's deep-sea counter-current to the Gulf Stream. The Americans contributed their

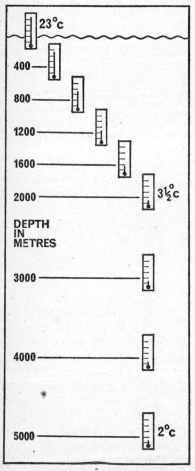

Fig. 72. The so-called 'thermocline' – the top layer of the oceans in which the temperature falls steadily with increasing depth below surface.

most refined techniques for the measurement of temperature and salinity; the British brought along the Swallow float, to be immediately dubbed the 'Pinger' by the American colleagues. Fig. 75 shows where they found the counter-current, of the predicted volume transport and at the predicted depth: namely 300-500 million kilograms of water per second, and 2,500 metres below sea surface.

And in November 1965, Bruce Heezen and two colleagues

Fig. 73. Stommel's idealized 'two-level' ocean. Let the eye follow the arrows and shadings through the complex pattern of ocean currents in the Atlantic, and it will pick out these salient features: the 'Antarctic Convergence' in the neighbourhood of 55°S, where ice-cold water flowing northwards in the upper layer from the neighbourhood of the Weddell Sea slants down beneath the rising bottom water from the far North Atlantic; the south-bound Brazil surface current, in the next level below which flows the attenuated continuation of the Gulf Stream counter-current; the Gulf Stream itself, flowing northwards atop its deep-level south-bound undercurrent, that meets and by-passes the upwelling Antarctic bottom current shorewards of Bermuda.

from Duke University took some remarkable under-water photographs of the sea bottom between Cape Hatteras and the island of Bermuda. There on the continental rise off the coast of North Carolina was revealed the scour of the Western Boundary Undercurrent, trending south-west; and over the sunken Bermuda Rise another set of scour marks, this time trending north-east, scribed by the dwindling Antarctic bottom current: both currents thus obeying the Coriolis force in their geostrophic flow.

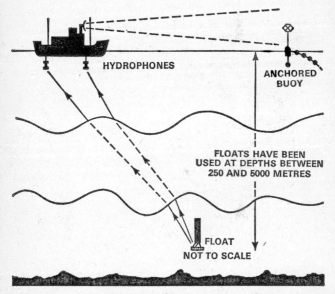

HYDROPHONES

ANCHORED BUOY

FLOATS HAVE BEEN USED AT DEPTHS BETWEEN 250 AND 5000 METRES

FLOAT NOT TO SCALE

Fig. 74. The 'Swallow Float', alias the 'Pinger'. The float consists of a bundle of hollow compressible aluminium tubes, which can be loaded to make the float 'neutrally buoyant' at a pre-chosen depth in sea water; it is in fact a sort of air-balloon in reverse. The float is let down over the side of the mother ship on two long wires – long enough to allow it to drift with the undersea current at the predetermined depth. The wires are connected each to one of two hydrophones installed below the keel of the mother ship, which is now hove-to head to wind. Its position is found and followed by means of radar 'fixes' on an anchored buoy; that of the float by noting the difference in time of arrival of sonar pulses from the float's built-in transmitter at the two hydrophones, as the mother ship falls away from the wind direction. (Original courtesy the British National Institute of Oceanography.)

The two deep-level currents differ, however, in that the Western Boundary Undercurrent (here of course still the Gulf Stream countercurrent) is strong and muddy, while the upwelling Antarctic bottom current is fast depositing its remaining load of sediments, and so is clear. Hence Heezen and the others got some stunning pictures of sponges and sea-pens on the sea-floor of the Rise, actually bending over downstream of the current, as well as clear-cut sediment streamers upstream of the dark-coloured manganese nodules that abound in this area of the ocean bottom.

Now these theories and discoveries of modern oceanography about the run of the deep-sea currents are of no mere academic interest. They are of vital importance to mankind in at least two directions.

First, there is the problem of the disposal of industrial radio-active waste in the atomic age. It is of no use light-heartedly to jettison the countless tons of it which will accumulate from the nuclear reactors of the future on the ocean bottom in mid-Atlantic, in the pious hope that it will stay there. We have only to look at Stommel's map, and concentrate on the points of down-welling in the sub-arctic and up-welling in the sub-antarctic, to realize that. No: we must first learn much more about the deep circulation of the oceans before we can say that here and here and here are safe places for the dumping of atomic waste.

Second, there is the literally crying need to garner the living harvest of the sea, that we may fill the hungry stomachs of an already overpopulated world. There must be a change-over from hunting to husbandry in the catching of fish. Fish, as any oceanographer will tell you, are the best oceanographers in the world. They know the ocean currents backwards. So must we, or perish: and in point of fact, the first concerted action by the world's oceanographers – the International Indian Ocean Expedition 1960–65 – on the then least known of the world's oceans, has been brought to a rather satisfactory conclusion.

Fig. 75. The counter-current to the Gulf Stream, predicted by Stommel in 1956 and found by *Discovery II* and *Atlantis* in April 1957.

The choice of the Indian Ocean for this pioneer exercise was made for four good reasons: First, the wind system of the Indian Ocean is governed by the seasonal monsoons, which change their direction every six months, from landward winds in winter to off-shore winds in summer. There was therefore here a great opportunity to make an independent test of the dynamics of Walter Munk's theory of ocean gyres, so successfully applied to the Atlantic and Pacific. Second, the prevalence of off-shore winds along several sectors of the coastline of the Indian Ocean for six months in every year. Such offshore winds pile up ocean water miles from the coast, leaving a hydrostatic deficit in the water column coastwards (Plate 23). This leads to the *upwelling* of bottom water to fill the hydrostatic 'vacuum', bringing nutrient salts to the surface which violently accelerate the rate of production o both plant and animal plankton in the surface waters, with a resultant enormous temporary increase in the population of edible fishes. A thorough exploitation of the yearly upwelling off the Arabian coast or in the Bay of Bengal could mean much to the protein-deficient populations in the lands bordering on what is potentially one of the richest fishing grounds in the world. Third, less was known about the topography of the floor of the Indian Ocean than that of the near side of the moon. And fourthly, marine biology – which needs no bush.

The suggestion for a mass attack on the Indian Ocean came from Columbus O'Donell Iselin at the inaugural meeting of the Special Committee on Oceanic Research (SCOR) of the International Council of Scientific Unions, held at Woods Hole Oceanographic Institute in New England in the fall of 1957. Now the members of SCOR are working scientists, planning for the professionally active oceanographers of the world. And plan they did, in the summer of 1960 at Helsinki and Copenhagen: they laid down in detail the programme of the IIOE, by and large as it was actually carried out between 1960 and 1965.

In the same year of 1960, however, an inter-governmental organization – the International Oceanographic Committee (IOC) – was created; and (to quote from the official record) 'the coordination of the IIOE was assumed by the IOC Secretariat in UNESCO House, Paris. The advisory role on aspects of the expedition remained with SCOR.'

Now to the results – and right away to the sad confession that the first item on the programme of the expedition was only very partially realized. In the words of the official write-up of the WMO (WMO – No. 166 TP81, Geneva, 1965), the meteorologists 'took some time to grasp the potential significance of the

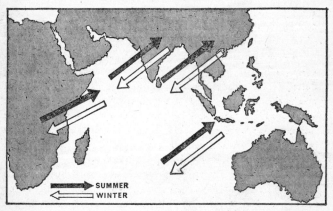

Fig. 76. The monsoons change direction each six months of the year.

programme to their discipline'. As a result, no systematic observation of the overall pattern of the wind-driven currents was achieved during the period of the expedition. On the credit side, however, must be recorded the establishment in 1963 by UNESCO of an International Meteorological Centre at the Colaba Observatory in Bombay, and the appointment of Colin Ramage of the University of Hawai as coordinator. His competent advice has remained at the disposal of the Centre after the close of the IIOE; and one may therefore expect considerable post-expedition activity on the meteorological side.

The exploration of some of the more important currents in the Indian Ocean got off to a flying start. Thus the British research ship *Discovery III* duly verified the presence of a sub-surface equatorial counter-current; and once again *Discovery* – this time in company with the Scripps research vessel *Argo* – as also the Russian *Vityaz*, made a preliminary reconnaissance of the Somali Current.

The Somali Current is the Indian Ocean equivalent of the North Atlantic Gulf Stream. From May to September it flows northwards, driven by the south-west monsoon, from the equator up along the east coast of Africa, as a narrow fast-flowing current which diverges eastward off the coast of Somaliland into the Arabian Sea. *Discovery*, besides making with *Argo* a preliminary survey of the surface current, established also the presence of a deep-level counter-current, flowing south at a depth of 1,000 metres with a speed of $1 \cdot 1 \times 10^2$ cm/sec, in full analogy with the flow pattern of the Gulf Stream. *Vityaz*, on the other hand, operating during the period of the *winter* monsoon, found a deep level *northward-bound* counter-current below the now south-ward-flowing surface current. Here then are exciting hints that both Munk and Stommel have something to say in the Indian Ocean; and one awaits the outcome of further work on the Somali Current with a certain impatience, and with a lively anticipation of great things to come.

An intensive study of upwelling off the South Arabian coast was made in the summer of 1963, during the period of the south-west monsoon, under the able direction of Ronald Currie, then at the British National Institute of Oceanography, now Director of the Marine Biological Laboratory at Millport on the Clyde.

Currie has given a lively account of the cruise of *Discovery III* out for upwelling in the Arabian Sea, in the *Geographical Magazine* (London) for July 1964, from which most of what follows here is taken. The south-west monsoon, veering to the east under the influence of the Coriolis force as it streams north from the equator, becomes a true off-shore wind along the coast of Southern Arabia. It brings foul weather with it, and the oil-tankers bound for Suez out of the ports on the Persian Gulf steer well clear of the coast when the monsoon blows. They have never seen the region of violent upwelling encountered by *Discovery* in that June of 1963, under leaden skies, on a sea shrouded in clammy fog, and with half a gale carrying the stink of dead fish with it; the water stained a reddish brown with millions of single-celled flagellates, or a dark blue-green with the needles of *Trichodesmium* algae.

Currie points up the apathy of the inhabitants of the countries bordering on the Arabian Sea, in their neglect to exploit the rich food chain presented to them by the salt-rich upwelling in a sea that beats upon their very doorstep. He contrasts the deserted Arabian Sea, where only dolphins feed on the fish which teem in the rich feeding grounds of the region of upwelling, with the bustle of the anchovy fisheries off the coasts of Peru, where there is a quite comparable upwelling; and he asks why factory ships don't ply across the Arabian Sea, from the summer-time area of upwelling off the South Arabian coast to the winter upwelling that must surely occur off the west coast of India and Pakistan during the period of the north-east monsoon.

Bruce Heezen, at the Royal Society of London Discussion on the Floor of the Northwest Indian Ocean, held on 12 November 1964, reported that 'as the result of the International Indian Ocean Exhibition, the bottom of the Indian Ocean is now one of the best-known areas of the ocean floor'; and he proceeded to tell the following tale:

The *continental slope* is scarred by two exceptionally large *canyons*, linked with the Indus and the Ganges. The *sediments* swept seawards by these two rivers are of such a volume that they pile up on the ocean floor as two great *abyssal cones*, shaped like a cone split in two and laid down horizontally with the base facing seaward – a feature found so far only in the Indian Ocean. The most conspicuous feature of the bottom topography is however the *Mid-Ocean Ridge*, lying like an inverted Y in the centre of the Indian Ocean floor. Flanking the rugged topography of the foot-hills of the ridge are the smoothest *abyssal plains* in the world, so flat that the echo sounder actually records the ocean swell as the research ship traverses them on the surface of the sea above!

Unique to the Indian Ocean are its *micro-continents*. Heezen lists the Madagascar Ridge, the Mascarene Plateau, the 'Ninety-east Ridge', the Chagos-Laccadive Plateau as the most prominent among them. Madagascar has, of course, long been recognized as continental in its rock structure; the remarkable case of the Chagos lavas has been discussed already in the previous chapter. The Ninetyeast Ridge is a newly discovered linear feature which

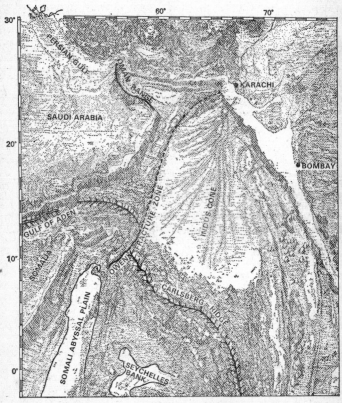

Fig. 77. The Arabian Sea. A portion of the Physiographic Diagram of the Indian Ocean, on which are pinpointed the Seychelles Bank, the Carlsberg Ridge with the Owen fracture zone, and the Gulf of Aden from among the features of the Arabian Sea referred to in the text. (Copyright © 1964 by Bruce C. Heezen and Marie Tharp; reproduced by permission.)

follows the line of longitude 90°E from 40°S northward into the Bay of Bengal. . . . There remains the Mascarene Plateau.

The submerged Mascarene Plateau lies north of Madagascar, surfacing at its northern end as the islands of the Seychelles group. The Seychelles have been rather thoroughly explored by the group from the Cambridge Department of Geodesy and Geophysics led by D. W. Matthews, operating from the British Hydrographic Vessel H.M.S. *Owen*. They have recorded numerous seismic profiles across the islands, have carried out magnetic and gravity surveys, and have examined rock specimens from the islands petrographically. And they have thus proved beyond a peradventure that the Seychelles rest on a basement of Pre-Cambrian granite, with a crustal thickness of 33 km: in other words, that the islands are a fragment of Africa.

The northern sector of the Carlsberg Ridge was explored as part of the Indian Ocean Expedition by Matthews and other members of the Cambridge Geophysical Laboratory in the spring of 1962, as already reported in Chapter 3 above. A year later, this time with Ben Browne as leader, H.M.S. *Owen* returned to the attack. A new feature was discovered on this cruise: namely, a *lateral displacement* of the ridge parallel to the South Arabian coast, which was named 'the Owen Fracture Zone' in recognition of the services of Her Majesty's Navy.

This discovery led to a detailed exploration of the floor of the Gulf of Aden by several national members of the IIOE, from which emerged an inescapable conclusion: that the cause of the lateral displacement of the Carlsberg Ridge is an anti-clockwise rotation by 8° of the entire Arabian Peninsula. This remarkable instance of continental drift, taking place as it were before one's very eyes, deserves a paragraph to itself.

The profile of the floor of the Gulf is a miniature version of that of the Atlantic Ocean – a central zone of rough topography, capped by a rift valley which marks the line of epicentres of a string of shallow eathquakes; flanked by two flat segments abutting at either side on the continental shelves of Somali and Saudi Arabia respectively. A high heatflow, anomalous mantle seismic velocity, and thin oceanic crust characterize the central ridge system. Magnetic anomalies which are similar in every detail to those of Fig. 51 march left and right of the rift valley, speaking to a lateral movement of the floor of the Gulf at the rate of 2 cm/yr, and dating the opening of the gulf as Miocene – that is, only 20 million years ago. Geological strata on opposing sectors of Saudi Arabia are a perfect match. And finally the Oman mountain range of eastern Arabia has been folded and overthrust during the Miocene-Pliocene. . . . So there you have it.

The chief aim of the Marine Biological Programme of the IIOE was to measure the productivity of the fishing grounds, actual and potential, of the Indian Ocean. To this end, a standard routine involving a Carbon-14 analysis of the first links in the food chain, that begins with the phytoplankton of the surface water and ends with edible fish (compare Plate 24), was worked out by Steeman Nielsen of Copenhagen. This ingenious technique relates the radio-active carbon present in standard samples of sea-water to its incorporation in the living cells of the phytoplankton and zooplankton, thanks to the photosynthesis of lifegiving carbon compounds by the hot sunshine of the tropics: whence it is handed on from the tiniest of crustaceans to the smallest of fishes, and so to the end-link represented by the giant tuna which are the mainstay of the Japanese fishing industry. The vast amount of material gathered in this ambitious programme takes time to analyse and collate; and it will be some years yet before a meaningful comparison can be made of the productivity in the numerous areas of the Indian Ocean from which samples of plankton have been taken.

A very important, indeed crucial point in the routine of sampling plankton in the surface waters is for everyone concerned to use a standard net and a carefully prescribed haul. The task of designing a standard sampling net and of framing a fixed procedure in carrying out the haul ('the standard net haul is a vertical haul from 200 metres to the surface ... the speed of hauling should be 1 metre/second' and so on) was assigned to Ronald Currie; and his 'Indian Ocean Standard Net' was used by the ships of all the major countries engaged in the biological programme of the Indian Ocean Expedition.

The taxonomical side of the plankton samples gathered from

far and wide over the Indian Ocean was not forgotten. The Indian government, in conjunction with UNESCO, established an Indian Ocean Biological Centre at Cochin in South India, under the care of the Danish marine biologist Vagn Hansen, who could report that a collection of 1,645 'net plankton samples' had been received at Ernakulam by the close of the year 1965.

In sober fact, the Indian Ocean Expedition has demonstrated once again, if that were needed, how readily men from a score of secular states can identify themselves with Man, when in the words of Friedhov Nansen 'he wants to know, and when he ceases to do so is no longer man' – in bitter contrast to his ant-like activities when he indeed so ceases: when he vomits on an environment of which he himself is part, and on the genes of his own loins, by spewing radio-active fall-out into his own atmosphere above Bikini, Christmas Island, Nova Zembla, Murarao and over the desert of Outer Mongolia.

Index

MORE ABOUT PENGUINS
AND PELICANS

Penguin Book News, an attractively illustrated magazine which appears every month, contains details of all the new books issued by Penguins as they are published. Every four months it is supplemented by *Penguins in Print*, which is a complete list of all books published by Penguins which are still available. (There are well over two thousand of these.)

A specimen copy of *Penguin Book News* can be sent to you free on request, and you can become a regular subscriber at 3s for twelve issues (with the complete lists). Just write to Dept EP, Penguin Books Ltd, Harmondsworth, Middlesex, enclosing a cheque or postal order, and your name will be added to the mailing list.

Some other books published by Penguins are described on the following pages.

Note: *Penguin Book News* and *Penguins in Print* are not available in the U.S.A. or Canada

THE FACE OF THE EARTH

G. H. Dury

The young natural science of geomorphology – the study of the form of the ground – is much less forbidding than its name. It is developing fast, and already promises to achieve some independence both of geology and of physical geography. In this book a professional geomorphologist tells how this field of knowledge is advancing, examines some of the hotly-disputed problems which have to be solved, and discusses the processes by which construction and erosion affect the physical landscape. Among the topics receiving attention are the weakening of rocks by weathering, their removal by the forces of erosion, the cyclic development of the land-surface, the evolution of river-systems, the effects of volcanic action and of glaciers, and the surface forms of deserts.

In choosing his examples, the author has been able to select freely from the results of his own field work. There are 102 diagrams in the text and 48 pages of plates.

UNDERSTANDING WEATHER

O. G. Sutton

This book, now revised and brought right up to date, with a new chapter on long-range forecasts, reflects the change in the approach to meteorology.

It outlines in simple terms the main features of climate and weather. The mysteries of warm and cold fronts, of isobars, anti-cyclones, and the rest, are all exposed. In addition, the book explains the *methods* which are needed to analyse the particularly complex data of meteorology. It gives a detailed account of daily forecasting, and shows how electronic computers will help in the future.

Can man forecast the weather a long way ahead, or even perhaps control it? Do nuclear tests affect it? These and many other relevant questions are discussed. The author is a professional meteorologist who seems to justify his claim that this subject is 'the most fascinating of all the earth sciences'.

APPLIED GEOGRAPHY

L. Dudley Stamp

Geography, literally 'writing about the earth', still means to far too many of us, influenced by school-day memories, the wearisome descriptions of countries in which lists of capes, bays, mountains, rivers, towns, and products play a major part. But its real interest is to describe and reflect the physical build and the natural resources, the sequence of human occupation and social organization, which have built the world we know, and will change and develop it in years to come. To know and understand these causes and their certain or probable effects is vital in all planning for the future; and this is the field of applied geography. In this book, a pioneer effort in its field, the principles of geographical survey and analysis are applied to the problems of Britain today.

DICTIONARY OF GEOGRAPHY

W. G. Moore

Our *Dictionary of Geography* – now revised and enlarged – describes and explains such commonly met terms as the Trough of Low Pressure (from the weather forecast), a Mackerel Sky, a Tornado, the Spring Tides, and hundreds of others. But there are also sections on such stranger phenomena as the Willy-willy of Australia, the Doctor of West Africa, the Plum Rains of Japan, the Volcanic Bomb, the Anti-Trades, the Bad Lands, and the Celestial Equator.

Because Geography is largely a synthetic subject, the items of the Dictionary are derived from many sciences, including geology, meteorology, climatology, astronomy, physics, anthropology, biology. Even the most abstruse terms, however, are of the kind that the student is likely to meet in the course of his reading – terms which the author of geographical works employs but often has no space to define. The dictionary may thus help to clarify and systematize the reader's knowledge.